It's another Quality Book from CGP

This book is for anyone doing Edexcel Modular
GCSE Mathematics at Higher Level.

It contains lots of tricky questions designed
to make you sweat — because that's the only
way you'll get any better.

It's also got some daft bits in to try and make
the whole experience at least vaguely
entertaining for you.

What CGP is all about

Our sole aim here at CGP is to produce the highest quality
books — carefully written, immaculately presented and
dangerously close to being funny.

Then we work our socks off to get them
out to you — at the cheapest possible prices.

Contents

Unit 1 — Statistics and Probability

Fractions, Decimals and Percentages 1
Percentages 2
Compound Interest and Depreciation.. 3
Ratios.. 5
Rounding and Estimating 6
Probability 8
Data Collection... 12
Types of Data.. 13
Sampling 14
Sampling Methods 15
Questionnaires.. 17
Mean, Median, Mode and Range 18
Quartiles and Interquartile Range 20
Frequency Tables 21
Grouped Frequency Tables 23
Cumulative Frequency.. 24
Histograms and Frequency Density 26
Scatter Graphs and Bar Charts 29
Spread of Data.. 31
Other Graphs and Charts... 32
Basic Algebra 34
Straight Line Graphs 35
Real-Life Graphs 38

Unit 2 — Number, Algebra and Geometry 1

Types of Number 39
Multiples, Factors and Prime Factors... 40
LCM and HCF... 42
Powers and Roots 43
Standard Index Form.. 45
Fractions and Decimals 46
Manipulating Surds and Use of π.. 48
More Algebra 49
Factorising Quadratics... 51
Sequences.. 52
Z Coordinates and Line Segments 53
$y = mx + c$ 54
More Graphs.. 55
Geometry... 56
Polygons 58
Symmetry and Circles 60
Areas and Nets 61
Volume and Projections.. 63
Metric and Imperial Units 64
Speed, Distance and Time 65

Unit 3 — Number, Algebra & Geometry 2

Calculating with Standard Index Form 66
Proportion and Variation 67
Percentage and Proportion Change 69
Bounds and Reciprocals 70
Solving Equations 72
Simultaneous Equations and Graphs 74
Simultaneous Equations 75
The Quadratic Formula 76
Completing the Square 77
Rearranging Formulas 78
Inequalities 80
Trial and Improvement 82
Quadratic Graphs 83
Some Harder Graphs to Learn 84
Graphs: Shifts and Stretches 86
Pythagoras' Theorem and Bearings 88
Pythagoras, Lines and Line Segments 89
Trigonometry — Sin, Cos, Tan 90
3D Pythagoras and Trigonometry 92
The Sine and Cosine Rules 93
More Circle Geometry 95
Vectors 97
"Real Life" Vector Questions 98
The Four Transformations 99
Congruence and Similarity 101
Loci and Construction 102
Circles, Cylinders and Spheres 104
Area, Volume and Density 107

Throughout the book, the more challenging questions are marked like this: **Q1**

Published by CGP
Illustrated by Ruso Bradley, Lex Ward and Ashley Tyson

From original material by Richard Parsons

Contributors: Gill Allen, JE Dodds, Sally Gill, Mark Haslam, C McLoughlin, John Waller, Janet West, Dave Williams.

Updated by: Sarah Blackwood, Rosie Gillham, Neil Hastings, Paul Jordin, Simon Little, Ali Palin, Ed Robinson, Julie Wakeling, Sarah Williams.

With thanks to Vicky Daniel and Sharon Keeley for the proofreading.

ISBN: 978 1 84762 094 1

Groovy website: www.cgpbooks.co.uk
Printed by Elanders Ltd, Newcastle upon Tyne.
Clipart sources: CorelDRAW® and VECTOR.

Fractions, Decimals and Percentages

I reckon that converting decimals to percentages is about as easy as it gets — so make the most of it.

Q1 Express each of the following as a percentage:

a) 0.25 c) 0.75 e) 0.4152 g) 0.3962

b) 0.5 d) 0.1 f) 0.8406 h) 0.2828

> All you're doing is multiplying by 100 — it really couldn't be easier.

Q2 Express each percentage as a decimal:

a) 50% c) 40% e) 60.2% g) 43.1%

b) 12% d) 34% f) 54.9% h) 78.8%

> Now you're dividing by 100 — so just move the decimal point to the left.

Q3 Express each of the following as a percentage:

a) $\dfrac{1}{2}$ d) $\dfrac{3}{4}$ g) $\dfrac{4}{15}$

b) $\dfrac{1}{4}$ e) $\dfrac{1}{25}$ h) $\dfrac{2}{7}$

c) $\dfrac{1}{8}$ f) $\dfrac{2}{3}$

> Convert each fraction to a decimal first on your calculator.

Q4 Express each percentage as a fraction in its lowest terms:

a) 25% e) 8.2%

b) 60% f) 49.6%

c) 45% g) 88.6%

d) 30% h) 32.4%

> Best thing to do with e)-h) is to put them over 100, then get rid of the decimal point by multiplying top and bottom by 10. Then just cancel down as normal.

Q5 119 out of 140 houses on an estate have DVD players. What percentage is this?

Q6 In an exam Tina scored 52/80. The grade she receives depends on the percentage scored. What grade will Tina get?

Grades	
51-60%	D
61-70%	C
71-80%	B
81-90%	A
91-100%	A*

Q7 Fill in the gaps in the following conversion table:

Fraction	Decimal
½	0.5
⅕	
	0.125
	1.6
⁴⁄16	
⁷⁄2	
	0.x
ˣ⁄100	
³⁄20	
	0.45

Percentages

Finding "something %" of "something-else" is really quite simple
— so you'd better be sure you know how.

Q1   Find:

a) 8% of £16   b) 85% of 740 kg   c) 40% of 40 minutes

Q2   A school has 750 pupils.

a) If 56% of the pupils are boys, what percentage are girls?
b) How many boys are there in the school?
c) One day, 6% of the pupils were absent. How many pupils was this?
d) 54% of the pupils have a school lunch, 38% bring sandwiches and the
    rest go home for lunch. How many pupils go home for lunch?

Q3   The owners of a museum are expecting a 14% increase in visitors next year.
    This year they had 20 200 visitors.
    How many visitors should they expect next year?

In this case you're looking at percentage change.

Q4   In a French test, Lauren scored 17/20. What percentage is this?

Q5   There are approximately 6000 fish and chip shops in the UK.
    On average, a fish and chip shop gets about 160 visitors each day.
    Given that the population of the UK is roughly 60 million, approximately
    what percentage of the population visit a fish and chip shop each day?

Q6   At birth, Veronica was 0.3 m tall. By adulthood she had grown to 1.5 m tall.
    Calculate her height now as a percentage of her height at birth.

Q7   Tanya paid £6500 for her new car. Each year its value decreased by 8%.
    How much was it worth when it was one year old?

Q8   Desmond's GCSE maths exam is next week. As part of his revision he attempted 31
    questions on his least favourite topic of percentages. He got 21 questions fully right
    on the first attempt. Two days later he tried all 31 questions again and this time got
    29 correct.

a) What percentage of questions did he get correct on his first attempt?
b) What percentage of questions did he get correct on his second attempt?
c) What is the percentage improvement in Desmond's results?

Compound Interest and Depreciation

Hey look — it's another of those "<u>there is only one formula to learn and you use it for every question</u>" topics.

So I reckon you'd better learn <u>The Formula</u> then...

Q1 A financial advisor is asked to predict the future value of his clients' investments. Calculate the amount in each of these accounts if:

a) £200 is invested for 10 years at 9% compound interest per annum

b) £500 is invested for 3 years at 7% compound interest per annum

c) £750 is invested for 30 months at 8% compound interest per annum

d) £1000 is invested for 15 months at 6.5% compound interest per annum.

Q2 A scientist is investigating a new strain of harmful bacteria. She needs to grow at least 4000 to have a big enough sample to run tests in the lab. The bacteria grows at the compound rate of 12% per hour, and she starts with 200 bacteria in the sample.

a) How many will there be after 3 hours?

b) How many will there be after 1 day?

c) After how many whole hours will there be at least 4000 bacteria?
(Solve this by trial and error.)

> Just make sure you get the <u>increase</u> and <u>decrease</u> the right way round... basically, just check your answer sounds like you'd expect — and if it doesn't, <u>do it again</u>.

Q3 An unknown radioactive element was discovered at the site of a suspected UFO crash. It was observed every day and the mass remaining was measured.
Initially there was 9 kg, but this decreased at the compound rate of 3% per day.
How much radioactive element was left after:

a) 3 days

b) 6 days

c) 1 week

d) 4 weeks?

Give your answers to no more than 3 d.p.

Q4 Money is invested on the stock market. During a recession the value of the shares fall by 2% per week. Find the value of the stock if:

a) £2000 was invested for a fortnight

b) £30 000 was invested for four weeks

c) £500 was invested for 7 weeks

d) £100 000 was invested for a year.

Q5 Mrs Smith decides to invest £7000 in a savings account. She has the choice of putting all her money into an account paying 5% compound interest per annum or she can put half of her investment into an account paying 6% compound interest per annum and the remaining half into an account paying 4% per annum.
If she left the investment alone for 3 years, which is her best option and by how much?

I'd put my money in Victorian rolling pins, myself...

Compound Interest and Depreciation

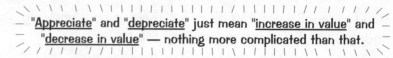

"Appreciate" and "depreciate" just mean "increase in value" and "decrease in value" — nothing more complicated than that.

Q6 An antique vase has increased in value since its owner bought it five years ago at £220. If its value has appreciated by 16% per year, how much is it worth today?

Q7 A small clothing company is about to go bust as business has been slow. When the owner started up four years ago she bought machinery costing £3500. The depreciation on this machinery is typically 2½% per year. How much money could the owner raise by selling this machinery now, second-hand?

Q8 The activity of a radio-isotope decreases at a compound rate of 9% every hour. If the initial activity is recorded at 1100 counts per minute, what will it be after:
  a) 2 hours
  b) 4 hours
  c) 1 day?
  d) The activity of the same radio-isotope is recorded at just 66 counts per minute. Using trial and error, estimate the length of time elapsed since the recording of 1100 counts per minute.

Q9 A used car salesman is buying stock at an auction. Before the auction, he estimates the value of each car on offer using their original price, their age, and a depreciation of 14% each year. This value is the maximum amount he will bid for each car. Calculate the maximum amount he should bid on these used cars:
  a) a car which cost £8495 six months ago
  b) a car which cost £34 000 eighteen months ago
  c) a car which cost £13 495 two years ago
  d) a car which cost £14 395 two years ago
  e) a car which cost £11 295 three years ago
  f) a car which cost £6 795 twelve months ago.

Q10 Property prices in one area have depreciated in value by 5% per year over the last three years. Calculate the expected value today of these properties, to the nearest pound:
  a) a house bought for £150 000, 3 years ago
  b) a bungalow bought for £115 000, 2 years ago
  c) a flat bought for £80 000, six months ago
  d) a factory bought for £500 000, 1 year ago.

Q11 A culture of bacteria increases in number at a compound rate of 0.4% per hour. If initially there was a culture of 50 cells, how many cells will there be after:
  a) 3 hours
  b) 8 hours 30 minutes
  c) 135 mins
  d) 2 days?

Q12 The population of a country is 16 million, and the annual compound growth rate is estimated to be 1.3%. Predict the country's population in:
  a) 4 years' time
  b) 20 years' time.

Ratios

I don't want to spoil the surprise, but you're going to need your calculator for this bit — get your finger on that fraction button...

RATIOS are like FRACTIONS which are like DECIMALS

We can treat the RATIO 3:4 like the FRACTION ¾, which is 0.75 as a DECIMAL.

Watch out though — this isn't ¾ of the total:
If there are girls and boys in the ratio 3:4, it means there's ¾ as many girls as boys.
So if there's 8 boys, there's ¾ × 8 = 6 girls.

Q1 Write these ratios in their simplest forms:
   a) 6:8   c) 1.5:3   e) 2 weeks:4 days
   b) 5:20   d) 2¼:4   f) £1.26:14p

Q2 A rectangle has sides in the ratio 1:2. Calculate the length of the longer side if the shorter side is:
   a) 3 cm   b) 5.5 cm   c) 15.2 m

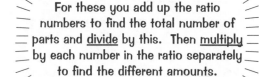

   Calculate the length of the shorter side if the longer side is:
   d) 3 cm   e) 5.5 cm   f) 15.2 m

Q3 Divide the following amounts in the ratios given:
   a) £20 in the ratio 2:3   c) 500 g in the ratio 1:2:2
   b) 150 m in the ratio 8:7   d) 8 hrs in the ratio 1:2:3

For these you add up the ratio numbers to find the total number of parts and divide by this. Then multiply by each number in the ratio separately to find the different amounts.

Q4 a) Increase £3.20 in the ratio 2:3.
   b) Decrease 120 cm in the ratio 3:2.

Q5 John and Peter share a bar of chocolate marked into 16 squares. They share it in the ratio 1:3 respectively. How many squares does each boy get?

Q6  A 2 litre bottle of cola is to be shared between three girls in the ratio 2:3:5. How many millilitres will each girl get?

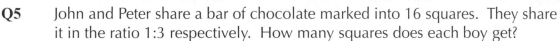

Watch out for your units — you'll have to change them over for this one — and your answer should be in millilitres.

Q7 Oak and ash saplings are planted along a roadside in the ratio 2:3 respectively. If there are 20 oak saplings, how many ash saplings are there?

Q8 Tony gives £100 to be shared by Jane, Holly and Rosemary in a ratio according to their age. Jane is 10, Holly is 12 and Rosemary is 3 years old. How much will each child get?

Q9 Sunil and Paul work in a restaurant. As they work different hours, they split their tips in the ratio 3:4. One night they got £28 in tips between them. Who got the most money from the tips and how much did they get?

Rounding and Estimating

Q1   Without using your calculator find approximate answers to the following:

a) 6560×1.97 g) 7139×2.13

b) 8091×1.456 h) $98 \times 2.54 \times 2.033$

c) $38.45 \times 1.4237 \times 5.0002$ i) $21 \times 21 \times 21$

d) $45.34 \div 9.345$ j) $8143 \div 81$

e) $34504 \div 7133$ k) $62000 \div 950$

f) $\dfrac{55.33 \times 19.345}{9.23}$ l) $\pi \div 3$

Turn these into nice easy numbers that you can deal with without a calculator.

Q2   At the start of the week, a shop had approximately 15 000 cartons of broccoli juice in stock. The shop sold 1483 cartons on Monday, 2649 on Tuesday, 1539 on Wednesday, 1478 on Thursday and 2958 on Friday. Estimate the number of cartons remaining.

Q3   Showing all your working, estimate the value of the following:

a) $\dfrac{144.5 + 49.1}{153.2 - 41.2}$ c) $\dfrac{2021.23 \times 4.0436}{20.33 \times 4.902}$

b) $\dfrac{18.2 \times 10.7}{\sqrt{398.6}}$ d) $\dfrac{(9.2)^2 \div 10.3}{4.306 \times 5.011}$

With all these rounding methods, you need to identify the last digit — e.g. if you're rounding 23.41 to 1 decimal place the last digit is 4. Then look at the next digit to the right. If it's 5 or more you round up, if it's 4 or less you round down.

Q4   Round these numbers to the required number of decimal places:

a) 62.1935 (1 dp)   d) 19.624328 (5 dp)

b) 62.1935 (2 dp)   e) 6.2999 (3 dp)

c) 62.1935 (3 dp)   f) π (3 dp)

Q5   Round these numbers to the required number of significant figures.

a) 1329.62 (3 SF)   d) 120 (1 SF)

b) 1329.62 (4 SF)   e) 0.024687 (1 SF)

c) 1329.62 (5 SF)   f) 0.024687 (4 SF)

Remember — the first significant figure is the first digit which isn't zero.

Rounding and Estimating

More rounding questions. Remember: 5 or more round up, 4 or less round down.

Q6 $K = 456.9873$
Write K correct to:

a) one decimal place

b) two decimal places

c) three decimal places

d) three significant figures

e) two significant figures

f) one significant figure.

Q7 Calculate the square root of 8. Write your answer to two decimal places.

Q8 Calculate, giving your answers to a sensible degree of accuracy:

a) $\dfrac{42.65 \times 0.9863}{24.6 \times 2.43}$

b) $\dfrac{13.63 + 7.22}{13.63 - 7.22}$

Q9 A bumper bag of icing sugar weighs 23.4 kg.
What is this correct to the nearest kilogram?

Q10 David divides £15.20 by 3.
What is the answer to the nearest penny?

Q11 The great racing driver Speedy Wheelman covered
234.65 miles during the course of one of his races.
Give this distance correct to the nearest mile.

Q12 Jack's company pays his travel expenses.
They round the distance he drives to the nearest mile, and then pay 20p for every mile.
In one week, Jack drives 95.45 miles. How much money can Jack claim back?

Q13 A pack of three model cars costs £14.30. John wants to work out what one
model car would cost. What is the answer correct to the nearest penny?

Q14 Pru measured the length of her bedroom as 2.345 metres.
Give this measurement correct to the nearest centimetre.

Probability

Probability can be a bit of a struggle — here's a quick reminder of the basics...

PROBABILITIES are always between 0 and 1

1) You should express probabilities as a <u>fraction</u> or a <u>decimal</u>.
2) A probability of <u>ZERO</u> means that it will <u>definitely not</u> happen.
3) A probability of <u>ONE</u> means it will <u>definitely</u> happen.

Q1 The number line opposite is a <u>probability scale</u>. Place the letters where you think the following statements lie, in terms of the <u>chance</u> of the event happening.

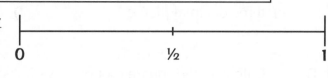

a) The probability of getting a <u>head</u> on a toss of a 10p piece.
b) The probability of <u>choosing a red ball</u> from a bag containing 2 red balls and 1 green ball.
c) The probability of shaking a <u>five</u> on an ordinary dice.
d) The probability of choosing a <u>Guatemalan stamp</u> from a bag containing 60 British stamps and 40 French stamps.

Q2 Debbie's employer organises a weekly prize draw, where the winning employee is selected at random. Debbie only joins in if her chance of winning is at least 0.1. If there are 8 other people playing this week, will Debbie choose to play?

SHORTHAND NOTATION

1) <u>P(x) = 0.25</u> simply means "<u>the probability of event x happening is 0.25</u>".
2) Eg: if you roll a dice, the <u>probability of rolling a 6</u> will be written as <u>P(rolls a 6)</u>.

Q3 After <u>49 tosses</u> of an unbiased coin, 24 have been heads and 25 have been tails. What is <u>P(50th toss will be a head)</u>?

Q4 If the probability of picking a banana from a fruit bowl is <u>0.27</u>, what is the probability of picking something which is <u>not</u> a banana?

Q5 A bag contains <u>3 red</u> balls, <u>4 blue</u> balls and <u>5 green</u> balls. A ball is chosen at random from the bag. What is the probability that:
a) it is green   c) it is red
b) it is blue   d) it is <u>not</u> red?

Q6 Students at school conduct a survey of the <u>colours</u> of parents' cars, where every parent owns one car. The table shows the results.

Red	Blue	Yellow	White	Green	Other
40	29	13	20	16	14

a) What is the probability of a parent owning a <u>red</u> car?
b) What is the probability of a parent owning a car that is <u>not</u> blue <u>or</u> green?

Q7 Draw a sample space diagram to show all the possible outcomes of throwing a standard dice and spinning this spinner:

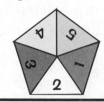

Probability

Q8 Charlton is making a bet with his friend before the local cricket team play a match. He thinks the match will end in a draw. A local newspaper prints the team's results over their last 20 matches, as shown.

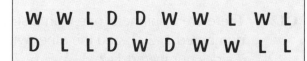

| W | W | L | D | D | W | W | L | W | L |
| D | L | L | D | W | D | W | W | L | L |

a) Complete the frequency table.

Outcome	Frequency
W	
D	
L	

b) Charlton reasons that since there are 3 possible results for any match, the probability that the next match will be drawn (D) is $\frac{1}{3}$. Explain why Charlton is wrong.

c) Suggest a value for the probability of a draw based on the team's past performance.

d) Based on their past performance, are the team most likely to win, lose, or draw?

Q9 **a)** What is the probability of randomly selecting either a black Ace or black King from an ordinary pack of playing cards?

b) If the entire suit of clubs is removed from a pack of cards, what is the probability of randomly selecting a red 7 from the remaining cards?

Remember the OR rule — P(A or B) = P(A) + P(B).

c) If all the 7s are also removed from the pack of cards, what is the probability of randomly selecting the 4 of diamonds?

Q10 For the roulette wheel shown, the probability of the ball landing on each of the numbers is listed in the table below.

Number	1	2	3	4	5	6
Probability	⅙	⅓	⅙	1/12	1/12	⅙

a) Find the probability of landing on an even number.

b) What is the probability of landing on black?

c) Why is the probability of landing on a white or a 3 not $\frac{5}{12} + \frac{1}{6}$?

Q11 The notepad below shows orders for 4 different sorts of rice at a certain Indian restaurant. Based on this data, what is the probability that the next order of rice is:

a) for pilau rice?

b) for spicy mushroom or special fried rice?

c) not for boiled rice?

If you're asked to work out probabilities based on some data, it's a <u>relative frequency</u> question.

boiled	20
pilau	24
spicy mushroom	10
special fried	6

Probability

Q12 There are 2 spinners: one with 3 sides numbered 1, 2, 3, and the other with 7 sides numbered 1, 2, 3, 4, 5, 6, 7.

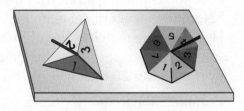

a) If both are spun together, list all the possible outcomes.

b) Complete the following table showing the sum of the 2 numbers for each outcome.

	1	2	3	4	5	6	7
1							
2							
3							

c) What is the probability that the sum is 6?
d) What is the probability that the sum is even?
e) What is the probability that the sum is greater than or equal to 8?
f) What is the probability that the sum is less than 8?
g) Explain how you can work out the probability in part **f)** without using the table.

Q13 3 balls are drawn at random, without replacement, from a bag containing 4 green balls and 3 red balls.

a) Complete the tree diagram below showing all the possible outcomes and their probabilities.

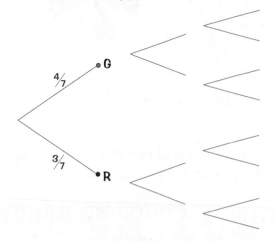

For AND you MULTIPLY along the branches.
For OR you ADD the end results.

b) What is the probability that exactly 2 green balls are drawn?
c) What is the probability that the last ball drawn is the same colour as the first?

Probability

Q14 How many times must you roll an ordinary 6-sided dice for the probability of getting at least one 6 to be more than 0.5?

> Don't forget the "<u>at least</u>" trick —
> <u>P(at least 1 six) = 1 – P(no sixes)</u>.

Q15 An unbiased dice in the shape of a tetrahedron has vertices numbered 1, 2, 3, 4. To win a game with this dice, you must throw a 4. At each go you have a maximum of 3 attempts.
  a) Using a tree diagram, calculate the probability of winning with the second throw of the first go.
  b) What is the probability of winning on the first go?

Q16 3 coins are drawn at random, without replacement, from a piggy bank containing 7 pound coins and 4 twenty-pence pieces.
  a) Draw a tree diagram showing all possible outcomes and their probabilities.
  b) Find the probability that the first coin selected is different in value from the third.
  c) Find the probability that less than £1.50 is drawn altogether.

Q17 Fabrizio is practising taking penalties. The probability that he misses the goal completely is $\frac{1}{8}$. The probability that the goalkeeper saves the penalty is $\frac{3}{8}$. The probability that he scores is $\frac{1}{2}$. Fabrizio takes two penalties.

  a) Calculate the probability that Fabrizio fails to score with his two penalties.
  b) Calculate the probability that he scores only one goal.
  c) Calculate the probability that Fabrizio scores on neither or both of his 2 attempts.

Q18 Trevor and his 2 brothers and 5 friends are seated at random in a row of 8 seats at the cinema. What is the probability that Trevor has one brother on his immediate left and one on his immediate right?

> Careful here — you have to include the probability
> that Trevor sits in one of the six middle seats.

Drawing a tree diagram might be a bit of a faff, but it can really help to make the question clearer. So if you're stuck, give the old tree diagram a try.

Data Collection

Q1 A headteacher wants to investigate how the exam timetable affects how well the students in her school do in exams. Write down two sub-questions that she could ask.

Q2 Say whether each of these data collection methods gives primary or secondary data.
a) Using data from the 1901 national census.
b) Doing an experiment to see how long students take to complete a puzzle.
c) Using temperature charts from a national newspaper.

Q3 In 1999, the Wonderme cosmetics company claimed that its anti-wrinkle cream was more effective than any other on the market. In 2003, a beauty salon used the Wonderme statistics when deciding which anti-wrinkle cream to promote.
a) Did the beauty salon use primary or secondary data?
b) Give two disadvantages of using these statistics.

Remember — you collect primary data yourself; secondary data is collected by someone else.

Q4 Some students are doing a project on recycling in their local area. They decide to ask this question:
Are recycling levels higher since the council set up a collection service?
a) What data could they use to answer this question?
b) State whether this is primary or secondary data.

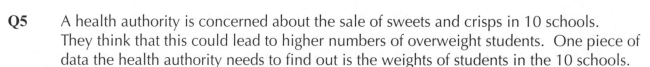

Q5 A health authority is concerned about the sale of sweets and crisps in 10 schools. They think that this could lead to higher numbers of overweight students. One piece of data the health authority needs to find out is the weights of students in the 10 schools.
a) Give another piece of data that's needed.
b) For each piece of data, should the health authority use primary or secondary data? Give reasons for your answers.
c) Suggest a suitable method of data collection the local authority could use to find out the weights of the students.

Q6 The local council wants to investigate whether or not road traffic accidents at a certain junction are more likely to occur during the morning rush hour (between 8 a.m and 9 a.m.) than any other time of day.

What data does the local council need to collect?

Types of Data

Data can be qualitative or quantitative, discrete or continuous — know the differences.

Q1 **a)** Write down a definition of quantitative data.
b) What is the name given to data which can't be measured numerically?

Q2 Zac collects some data about his school. The data items are listed below.
Say whether each data item is qualitative or quantitative.

a) The colours of pants worn by the teachers.
b) The number of students late to school from each form on the first day of term.
c) The distance travelled to school by each student.
d) The star sign of each student.

Q3 **a)** What name is given to quantitative data that can be measured exactly?
b) Give one example of this type of data.
c) Write down a definition of continuous data.
d) Give one example of continuous data.

Q4 A music shop sells CDs, DVDs, tapes and some vinyl records.
State one example of qualitative data that could be collected by the shop.

Q5 Amy collects some data at her school sports day. The data items are listed below.
Say whether each data item is discrete or continuous.
a) The number of competitors in each event.
b) The finishing times of each competitor in the 100-metre sprint.
c) The total number of points scored by each form at the end of the day.
d) The distances jumped by each competitor in the long jump.

If you're doing stats, you often end up with loads and loads of data, which can be pretty hard to analyse. It helps to group it together, so it's more manageable.

Q6 Fred asked each of his 30 classmates how long (in minutes) it took them to eat their dinner. Here are the results he recorded:

42 13 6 31 15 20 19 5 50 14
8 25 16 27 4 45 32 31 31 10
32 17 16 19 29 42 43 30 29 18

a) Group the data appropriately and fill in the table.
b) State one disadvantage of grouping data.

Length of time (mins)					
Number of people					

Sampling

 Make sure you know what your population is — you can't do anything without knowing that.

Q1   Write down the definition of the term 'population'.

Q2   Say what the population is for each of these surveys:
  a) The health effects of smoking on 20- to 30-year-old women.
  b) The average number of trees in public parks in London.
  c) The average number of hours British squirrels spend juggling nuts.
  d) The pay of football players in the Premier League.

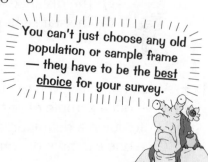
You can't just choose any old population or sample frame — they have to be the <u>best</u> <u>choice</u> for your survey.

Q3   An environmental group is investigating the water quality in all the lakes and ponds in Nottingham.
  a) What population should the environmental group use?
  b) What should they use as a sample frame?

Q4   Professor Xavier Entric is doing a research project on the lifespan of moorland dung beetles in the UK.

  a) What population would Professor Entric use for his research?
  b) Give one reason why Professor Entric would use a sample, rather than surveying the whole population.

Q5   James wants to know the average weekly wage earned by teenagers in his town. He calculates the mean from the weekly wages of three of his classmates at school.

Give two reasons why this sample may not give him a true estimate of the average wage for teenagers in the town.

Q6   Whitby Football Club are trying to find out about how much their supporters are prepared to spend on merchandise.
  a) What population should Whitby Football Club sample from?
    The football club prepare a questionnaire and send it to 1000 people chosen at random from the electoral register (a list of all the people registered to vote) of Whitby.
  b) What population have Whitby Football Club used as a sample frame?
  c) Give one criticism of the way that Whitby Football Club have chosen their sample.

Sampling Methods

The **key** to really good sampling is a __well-defined__ population and a sample frame — it's important these are right so that your results are __representative__ of the population.

Q1 What does choosing something at "random" mean?

Q2 Random numbers can be generated using a random number table. Give two other ways of generating random numbers.

Q3 A bakery makes 50 Battenberg cakes every day.
The quality controller tests the cakes every Friday for weight and tastiness.
She can only use a sample of 5 cakes because the cakes get eaten in the tastiness test.

a) Each week the quality controller chooses the first 5 cakes off the production line for her sample. What is wrong with this method?

b) On one Friday, all the cakes are weighed, giving the following results:

201 g	203 g	206 g	194 g	203 g	194 g	208 g	194 g	203 g	184 g
206 g	197 g	196 g	206 g	189 g	198 g	204 g	196 g	199 g	204 g
205 g	201 g	211 g	222 g	204 g	194 g	203 g	198 g	199 g	194 g
212 g	195 g	206 g	202 g	198 g	206 g	201 g	205 g	201 g	194 g
198 g	197 g	204 g	203 g	201 g	205 g	202 g	199 g	195 g	198 g

Describe how you would choose a simple random sample of 5 cake weights.

Q4 The Instyle chain of hair salons employs 1000 people across the UK. Of these, 99 are receptionists, 53 are salon managers, 251 are colour technicians and the rest are stylists. They decide to use a stratified sample of 100 to find out about employee satisfaction.

a) How many of each type of employee should be in the sample?

b) Give one reason why it is better for the Instyle chain to use a stratified random sample than a simple random sample.

Q5 Fred is doing a statistical project on the distances travelled by students to his school. The table below gives a breakdown of the numbers of students in each year group at Fred's school.

Year Group	7	8	9	10	11
Number of Students	398	405	401	197	199

Don't forget that the proportion of a group in a sample has to be the same as the proportion of that group in the population.

Fred decides to take a stratified random sample with 40 students,

a) Give a reason why Fred has decided to choose a stratified sample.

b) How many Year 7 students would be in the sample?

c) In another stratified random sample from the same school, there are ten Year 11 students. How many students are in this sample altogether?

Sampling Methods

 Most of these samples have been taken from the <u>wrong population</u>. You need to work out the <u>target population</u> and compare it to the one that is sampled.

Q6 Millom University Chemistry Department wants to find out the influence of its marketing on sixth-form chemistry students in the UK. They compile a survey and send it to all the students at the nearest sixth-form college.

  a) Give two reasons why this sample is biased.

  b) What population should the Millom University Chemistry Department be sampling from?

Q7 The Cheapeez discount food chain wants to find out what products to stock to attract more of the residents of Devon. Their interviewers survey the first 200 people to go into five Cheapeez supermarkets in Devon on the first Saturday in March.

  a) Give one reason why this sample will produce biased data.

  b) What population should have been sampled from?

Q8 The table below shows a breakdown of the age groups of the residents of Yeovil.

Age	Under 18	18-30	31-40	41-60	Over 60
Percentage of population	23%	17%	12%	32%	16%

The local council wants to find out whether their residents prefer to shop at out-of-town shopping centres or on Yeovil High Street. They put together a questionnaire and interview a sample of 1000 people shopping on Yeovil High Street on Saturday morning. The sample contains 205 people aged 30 or under, 421 people aged 31 to 40, 199 people aged 41 to 60 and 175 over-60s.

  a) Write down two reasons why this sample is biased.

  b) What population should the council have sampled from?

Q9 Fred is trying to find out why people use public transport.
He surveys a sample of 100 people passing through the town bus station between 5.30 p.m. and 6.30 p.m. on a Monday evening.

  a) Give one reason why Fred's sample is biased.

  b) Say how Fred could improve his sample to avoid bias.

Q10 Give a reason why the following methods of sampling are poor:

  a) a survey carried out inside a newsagents concluded that 80% of the population buy a daily newspaper

  b) a phone poll conducted at 11 am on a Sunday morning revealed that less than 2% of the population regularly go to church

  c) 60% of the population were estimated to watch the 9 o'clock news each evening after a survey was carried out at a bridge club.

Questionnaires

Questionnaires are a great way to gather information. But you need to think carefully about how you design, distribute and collect them so you get the information you want.

Q1 Stanley is researching the use of the school canteen.
He asks this question to a sample of students at the school:
How often do you use the canteen? Tick one of the boxes.

Very often ☐   *Quite often* ☐

Not very often ☐   *Never* ☐

   a) Give one criticism of Stanley's question.
   b) Write a question that Stanley could use to find out how often students at his school use the canteen.

Q2 A local council wants to find out how they can attract businesses to their area.
They design a questionnaire which includes this question:
How many employees at your company watch soap operas?
Give one criticism of this question.

Q3 A drinks company is trying to profile their customers. They want to find out which age groups to target their marketing at. They use this question as part of a questionnaire:
How old are you?
i) Under 18   ii) 18 to 30   iii) 30 to 40   iv) 40 to 60   v) over 60
   a) Give one criticism of this question.
   b) How would you improve this question?

Q4 Peter compiles a questionnaire on music tastes and sends it to a sample of 100 students at his school. He receives 55 questionnaires back.
   a) State one problem that Peter could have with his data.
   b) What could Peter do to avoid this problem?

Q5 Pauline is the manager of a small café. She knows that some of her customers buy cold drinks from the cold drinks machine, some buy hot drinks from the hot drinks machine and some people buy snacks and drinks at the counter.
Pauline would like to use a questionnaire to find out whether she should stock a new brand of cola. Here is part of Pauline's questionnaire:

Café Questionnaire

1) Please tick the box to show how often you visit the café:

daily ☐   weekly ☐   fortnightly ☐   monthly ☐   less than monthly ☐

   a) Using the same style, design another question that Pauline could include in her questionnaire.
   b) Pauline hands out her questionnaire as she serves customers at the counter. Give a reason why this is a suitable or unsuitable way to hand out the questionnaire.

Mean, Median, Mode and Range

For finding the <u>mode</u> and <u>median</u> put the data in order of size — this makes it much easier to find the most frequent and middle values.

The <u>mean</u> involves a bit more calculation, but hey, you're doing maths...

Q1 The local rugby team scored the following number of tries in their first 10 matches of the season:

3	5	4	2	0	1	3	0	3	4

Find their modal number of tries.

Q2 Find the mean, median, mode and range of these numbers:

1	2	–2	0	1	8	3	–3	2	4	–2	2

Q3 A company has 9 employees in the sales department who earn commission. They are advertising for another salesperson and want to say in the advert how much commission their staff earn on average. The amount of commission the 9 existing salespeople earned last year is as follows:

£13,000	£9,000	£7,500
£18,000	£12,000	£7,500
£23,000	£15,000	£11,500

a) Find the mean, median and mode of their earnings.
b) Which one does not give a good indication of their average commission?
c) Which should the company put in the advert, and why?

Q4 Molly is writing a letter of complaint to the bus company because she thinks her bus to school is regularly late. Over 3 weeks, Molly kept a record of how many minutes her bus was either early or late, and put this in her letter. (She used + for late and – for early.)

+2	–1	0	+5	–4
–7	0	–8	0	+4
–4	–3	+14	+2	0

a) Calculate the mean lateness/earliness of the bus.
b) Calculate the median.
c) What is the mode?
d) The bus company use the answers to **a)**, **b)** and **c)** to claim they are always on time. Is this true?

Careful with this — you have to use the averages to find the total weight, then divide to find the new average.

Q5 The average weight of the 11 players in a football team was 72.5 kg. The average weight of the 5 reserve players was 75.6 kg. What was the average weight of the whole squad? (Give your answer to 3 s.f.)

Q6 The mean daily weight of potatoes sold in a greengrocer's from Monday to Friday was 14 kg. The mean daily weight of potatoes sold from Monday to Saturday was 15 kg. How many kg of potatoes were sold on Saturday?

Mean, Median, Mode and Range

Q7   Colin averaged 83% over 3 exams. His average for the first two exams was 76%.
What was Colin's score in the final exam?

Q8   The range for a certain list of numbers is 26, one of the numbers in the list is 48.
   a) What is the lowest possible value a number in the list could be?
   b) What is the highest possible value that could be in the list?

Q9   An ordinary dice is rolled 6 times, landing on a different number each time.
   a) What is the mean score?
   b) What is the median score?
   c) What is the range of scores?

Q10   The bar graph shows the amount of time Jim and Bob spend
watching TV during the week.

   a) Find the mean amount of time per
day each spends watching TV.

   b) Find the range of times for each of
them.

   c) Using your answers from **a)** and **b)**,
comment on what you notice about
the way they watch TV.

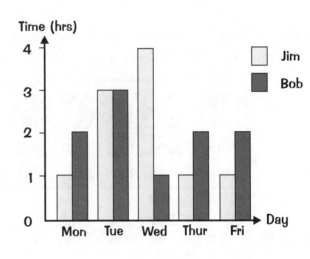

Q11   Mr Jones posted 88 Christmas cards first class on
Monday. His friends received them over the week:
40 on Tuesday, 28 on Wednesday, 9 on Thursday,
6 on Friday and the remainder on Saturday.
   a) Find the modal number of days it took for the cards
to arrive.
   b) Find the median number of days it took for the cards
to arrive.
   c) "The majority of first class post arrives within 2
days." Is the above statement true or false in the
light of the data?

Q12   In each of the following cases, decide which average is referred to:
   a) this average is least appropriate when the total number of values is small
   b) this average is least affected if one of the values is removed at random
   c) this average is most affected by the presence of extreme values.

Quartiles and Interquartile Range

Remember to put the data in <u>ascending</u> order before you work out where the quartiles come in a list.

Q1   The weights (in g) of 29 eggs are:

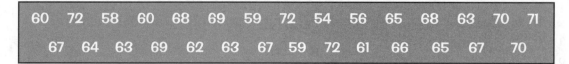

| 60 | 72 | 58 | 60 | 68 | 69 | 59 | 72 | 54 | 56 | 65 | 68 | 63 | 70 | 71 |
| 67 | 64 | 63 | 69 | 62 | 63 | 67 | 59 | 72 | 61 | 66 | 65 | 67 | 70 | |

a) What is the median?
b) Which quartile is equivalent to the median?

Q2   The following table shows the number of cars parked in a multi-storey car park at midday on each day in December:

690	720	580	590	210	650	640	710
700	750	790	220	790	840	830	820
900	880	480	1000	990	1020	1010	1000
80	240	370	510	460	600	580	

a) What is the range?
b) What is the lower quartile, Q_1?
c) What is the median?
d) What is the upper quartile, Q_3?

Quartiles divide the data into 4 equal groups.

Q3   For all the whole numbers from 1 to 399 inclusive:

What is the interquartile range?

The interquartile range tells you the range of the middle 50% of the data.

Q4   The range of 99 different integers is 98, and the median is 350.

a) What is the lower quartile, Q_1?
b) What is the interquartile range?

Frequency Tables

You've got to be able to do these in both row and
column form, because they could give you either one.
There's no real difference, and the rules are still the same.

Q1 To monitor their annual performance, a travel company logs all calls to their sales desk.
The number of calls per day received by the sales desk over a given year are shown here.

No. of Calls	10	11	12	13	14	15	16 and over
No. of Days	110	70	120	27	18	12	8

a) Find the median number of calls.
b) Find the modal number of calls.
c) Find the interquartile range.

Q2 A student has classes in Mathematics (M),
English (E), French (F), Art (A) and Science (S).
Her timetable is shown opposite.

Monday	S S E E A
Tuesday	E M M A A
Wednesday	S M E F F
Thursday	F E E A S
Friday	M M E S S

a) Complete the following frequency table for a week's lessons:

b) Calculate the number of French
lessons that the student will attend
during a 12-week term.

Subject	M	E	F	A	S
Frequency					

c) What is the modal lesson?

Q3 20 pupils are asked to estimate the length (to the nearest m) of their gardens.
Here are the results: 10, 8, 6, 4, 10, 8, 0, 14, 12, 8, 10, 6, 1, 6, 10, 8, 6, 6, 8, 8
Copy the frequency table below and put the estimates in.

a) Find the mode of the data.
b) Find the median of the data.
c) State the range of the data.

Length (m)	4 and under	6	8	10	12	14 and over
Frequency						

Frequency Tables

Q4   130 female bus drivers were weighed to the nearest kg.
Calculate:
- **a)** the median weight
- **b)** the interquartile range of the weights
- **c)** the modal weight
- **d)** the mean weight, by first completing the table.

Weight (kg)	Frequency	Weight × Frequency
51	40	
52	30	
53	45	
54	10	
55	5	

Q5   A football magazine rates teams according to how many goals they're likely to score in a match, based on their last 20 matches. The table below shows the number of goals scored by Spark Bridge Wanderers over this period.

No. of goals	0	1	2	3	4	5	6
Frequency	0	1	1	7	6	3	2

Find the mean, mode and median of the data.

Q6   A tornado has struck the hamlet of Moose-on-the-Wold. Many houses have had windows broken. The frequency table shows the devastating effects.

No. of windows broken per house	0	1	2	3	4	5	6
Frequency	5	3	4	11	13	7	2

- **a)** Calculate the modal number of broken windows.
- **b)** Calculate the median number of broken windows.
- **c)** Calculate the mean number of broken windows.

Q7   Using the computerised till in a shoe shop, the manager can predict what stock to order from the previous week's sales.
Opposite is the tabulated printout for last week for men's shoes.

Shoe size	5	6	7	8	9	10	11
frequency	9	28	56	70	56	28	9

- **a)** The mean, mode and median for this data can be compared. For each of the following statements decide whether it is true or false.
  - **i)**   The mode for this data is 70.
  - **ii)** The mean is greater than the median for this distribution.
  - **iii)** The mean, median and mode are all equal in this distribution.
- **b)** What percentage of customers bought shoes of the mean size from last week's sales data:
  - **i)** 30%   **ii)** 70%   **iii)** 0.273%   or   **iv)** 27.3%?

Grouped Frequency Tables

Q1   The speeds of 32 skiers at a certain corner of a downhill course are tabulated below.

Speed (km/h)	$40 \leq s < 45$	$45 \leq s < 50$	$50 \leq s < 55$	$55 \leq s < 60$	$60 \leq s < 65$
Frequency	4	8	10	7	3
Mid-Interval					
Frequency × Mid-Interval					

a) By completing the frequency table, estimate the mean speed.
b) How many skiers were travelling at less than 55 km/h?
c) How many skiers were travelling at 50 km/h or faster?

Q2   The weights in kg of 18 newly felled trees are noted below:
272.7   333.2   251.0   246.5   328.0   259.6   200.2   312.8   344.3
226.8   362.0   348.3   256.1   232.9   309.7   398.0   284.5   327.4

a) Complete the frequency table.

Weight (kg)	Tally	Frequency	Mid-Interval	Frequency × Mid-Interval
$200 \leq w < 250$				
$250 \leq w < 300$				
$300 \leq w < 350$				
$350 \leq w < 400$				

b) Estimate the mean weight using the frequency table.
c) What is the modal class?

Q3   48 numbers are recorded below:

0.057   0.805   0.056   0.979   0.419   0.160   0.534   0.763
0.642   0.569   0.773   0.055   0.349   0.892   0.664   0.136
0.528   0.792   0.085   0.546   0.549   0.908   0.639   0.000
0.614   0.478   0.421   0.472   0.292   0.579   0.542   0.356
0.070   0.890   0.883   0.333   0.033   0.323   0.544   0.668
0.094   0.049   0.049   0.999   0.632   0.700   0.983   0.356

a) Transfer the data into the frequency table.

Number	$0 \leq n < 0.2$	$0.2 \leq n < 0.4$	$0.4 \leq n < 0.6$	$0.6 \leq n < 0.8$	$0.8 \leq n < 1$
Tally					
Frequency					
Mid-Interval					
Frequency × Mid-Interval					

b) Write down the modal class(es).
c) Which class contains the median?
d) Estimate the mean value.

Cumulative Frequency

Q1   Using the cumulative frequency curve,
read off the:
a) median
b) lower quartile
c) upper quartile
d) interquartile range
e) the frequency below $x = 130$.

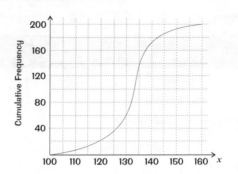

Q2   The following box plot shows the ages in years of trees in a wood.

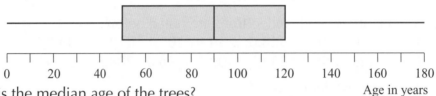

a) What is the median age of the trees?
b) What is the upper quartile value?
c) What is the interquartile range?

Q3   The number of passengers using a bus service each day has been recorded over a
4-week period. The data is presented in the table below:

No. passengers	$0 \leq n < 50$	$50 \leq n < 100$	$100 \leq n < 150$	$150 \leq n < 200$	$200 \leq n < 250$	$250 \leq n < 300$
Frequency	2	7	10	5	3	1
Cumulative Frequency						
Mid-Interval						
Frequency × Mid-Interval						

A mean passenger

a) By completing the table, estimate the mean number of passengers.
b) By plotting a cumulative frequency curve, determine the median value.
c) What is the modal class?

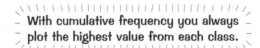

With cumulative frequency you always
plot the highest value from each class.

Q4   40 pupils have taken an exam and their marks are recorded in a frequency table.

Mark (%)	$0 \leq m < 20$	$20 \leq m < 40$	$40 \leq m < 60$	$60 \leq m < 80$	$80 \leq m < 100$
Frequency	2	12	18	5	3
Cumulative Frequency					

a) Complete the table and plot the cumulative frequency curve.
b) What is the value of the lower quartile?
c) What is the interquartile range?
d) What is the median mark?

Cumulative Frequency

Q5   One hundred scores for a board game are presented in the table below.

Score	$31 \le s < 41$	$41 \le s < 51$	$51 \le s < 61$	$61 \le s < 71$	$71 \le s < 81$	$81 \le s < 91$	$91 \le s < 101$
Frequency	4	12	21	32	19	8	4
Cumulative Frequency							

a) What is the modal class?
b) Which group contains the median score?
c) By plotting the cumulative frequency curve determine the actual value of the median score.
d) Find the interquartile range.

Q6   The following frequency table gives the distribution of the lives of electric bulbs.

a) Complete the frequency table.

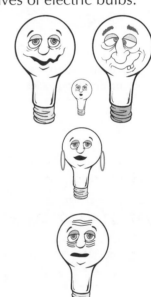

Life (hours)	Frequency	Cumulative Frequency
$900 \le L < 1000$	10	
$1000 \le L < 1100$	12	
$1100 \le L < 1200$	15	
$1200 \le L < 1300$	18	
$1300 \le L < 1400$	22	
$1400 \le L < 1500$	17	
$1500 \le L < 1600$	14	
$1600 \le L < 1700$	9	

b) Which group contains the median value?
c) By drawing the cumulative frequency curve, find the actual value of the median.
d) Determine values for the upper and lower quartiles.

Q7   30 pupils recorded the time taken (minutes : seconds) to boil some water.
Here are their results: 2:37 2:37 3:17 3:30 2:45 2:13 3:18 3:12 3:38 3:29
                              3:04 3:24 4:13 3:01 3:11 2:33 3:37 4:24 3:59 3:11
                              3:22 3:13 2:57 3:12 3:07 4:17 3:31 3:42 3:51 3:24

a) By using a tally, transfer the data into the frequency table.

Time	$2:00 \le t < 2:30$	$2:30 \le t < 3:00$	$3:00 \le t < 3:30$	$3:30 \le t < 4:00$	$4:00 \le t < 4:30$
Tally					
Frequency					
Cumulative Frequency					

b) Draw the cumulative frequency curve.
c) Using your graph, read off the median and the upper and lower quartiles.
d) What is the interquartile range?

Histograms and Frequency Density

It's the <u>size that counts</u>... You've got to look at the <u>area</u> of the bars to find the frequency. That means looking at the <u>width</u> as well as the height.

Q1 The Bog Snorkelling Appreciation Society conducts a survey on the ages of all their members. The histogram below shows the age distribution of the people surveyed. The Society organises a 'Seniors' bog snorkelling event for members aged 60 or older. Use the graph to estimate the maximum number of people that might take part.

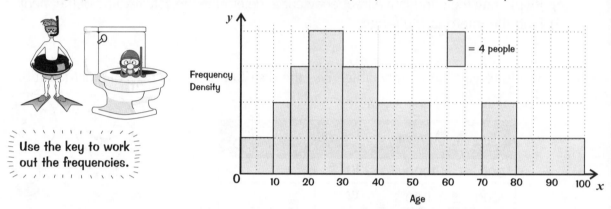

Use the key to work out the frequencies.

Q2 I did a survey to find out how many living relatives my friends have.
Here are my results:

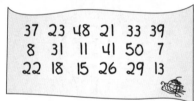

37 23 48 21 33 39
8 31 11 41 50 7
22 18 15 26 29 13

Draw a stem and leaf diagram to represent this data.
Use this key:

Key: 1 | 4 means 14

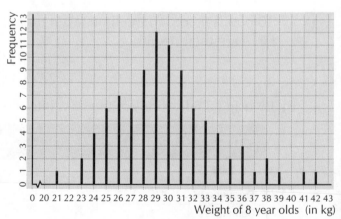

Q3 a) Use the information from this line graph to create your own stem and leaf diagram, using class-widths of 5. Then make a key to show how to use your diagram.

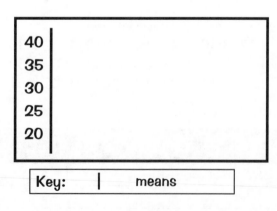

40
35
30
25
20

Key: | means

Frequency / Weight of 8 year olds (in kg)

b) From your diagram, find:
  i) the range of the data
  ii) the median of the data.

Histograms and Frequency Density

Q4 The weight of honey collected from several beehives is tabulated below.

a) Complete the frequency table by calculating the frequency densities.
b) Draw a histogram to represent this data.
c) Use your histogram to estimate the number of beehives that produced more than 6 kg of honey.

Weight (kg)	$0 \leq w < 2$	$2 \leq w < 4$	$4 \leq w < 7$	$7 \leq w < 9$	$9 \leq w < 15$
Frequency	3	2	6	9	12
Frequency density					

Q5 A group of sixth formers took part in a survey to see how much time they spent watching TV each week. The results were recorded in this histogram.

a) Complete the table by filling in the frequency density and frequency columns.

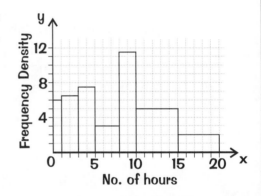

No. of hours	Frequency density	Frequency
$0 \leq h < 1$		
$1 \leq h < 3$	6.5	13
$3 \leq h < 5$		
$5 \leq h < 8$		
$8 \leq h < 10$		
$10 \leq h < 15$		
$15 \leq h < 20$		

b) How many students took part in the survey?
c) Estimate the number of students that watch more than 7, but less than 13 hours of TV each week.

Q6 A local newspaper employee has collected data on the salaries of 100 people living in the area. His data is shown in the table below.

Salary (£1000s)	$0 \leq s < 10$	$10 \leq s < 20$	$20 \leq s < 30$	$30 \leq s < 40$	$40 \leq s < 50$
Frequency	10	25	42	20	3
Frequency Density					

a) Complete the table and draw a histogram to show the data.
b) The newspaper prints this histogram alongside the one shown on the right. It represents data from an identical survey done 10 years earlier. Write a comment comparing current salaries and those from 10 years ago.

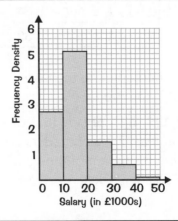

Histograms and Frequency Density

Q7   A farmer keeps track of the amount of milk produced by his cows each day.

Amount of Milk (Litres)	Frequency	Frequency Density	Mid-Interval	Frequency × Mid-Interval
$0 < C < 1$	6			
$1 \leqslant C < 5$	6			
$5 < C < 8$	6			
$8 < C < 10$	6			
$10 < C < 15$	6			
$15 < C < 20$	6			

a) Complete the frequency table.
b) Use the mid-interval technique to estimate the mean.
c) Draw a histogram to show the data.
d) On how many days is less than 8 litres produced?

Q8   The publishers of a teen magazine want to increase its price.
To help them choose the best price, they carried out a survey of
188 readers to see how much pocket money they receive each week.

Amount (£)	Frequency	Frequency Density	Mid-Interval	Frequency × Mid-Interval
$0 \leq A < 0.50$	11			
$0.50 \leq A < 1.00$	25			
$1.00 \leq A < 1.30$	9			
$1.30 \leq A < 1.50$	12			
$1.50 \leq A < 1.80$	24			
$1.80 \leq A < 2.50$	21			
$2.50 \leq A < 3.10$	54			
$3.10 \leq A < 4.10$	32			

a) By first completing the table, estimate the mean amount of pocket money.
b) What is the modal class?

   The publishers decide that £1.40 would be a reasonable price, but they want to check
   that at least 75% of readers could afford to buy the magazine with their pocket money.
c) Draw a histogram of the data and estimate how many readers receive less than £1.40.
d) Do 75% of readers receive £1.40 or more?

Scatter Graphs and Bar Charts

A **SCATTER GRAPH** is just a load of points on a graph that <u>end up in a bit of a mess</u>, rather than in a nice line or curve. There's a fancy word to say how much of a mess they're in — it's <u>CORRELATION</u>.

Q1 Match the following diagrams with the most appropriate descriptive label.

Labels: (P) Strong positive correlation   (S) Moderate negative correlation
         (Q) Exact negative correlation   (T) Medium correlation
         (R) Little or no correlation   (U) Exact positive correlation.

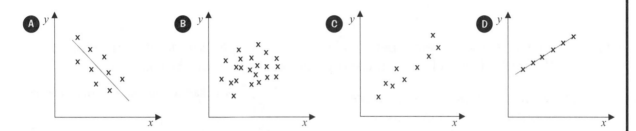

Q2 Adam thinks that cricketers who are good at batting must also be good at bowling. The bowling and batting averages for the members of his local team are given in the table.

Batting	8	13	17	26	29	35	37	40	45	52	57
Bowling	32	13	22	31	14	22	6	10	50	39	12

a) Draw a scatter diagram for the above data.

b) State the type of correlation, if any.

c) Is Adam correct in his assumption? Explain your answer.

> Good batters have a <u>high</u> batting average.
> Good bowlers have a <u>low</u> bowling average.

Q3 The examination results (%) for a class of students for 2 exams are shown in the table.

Physics	97	61	36	56	48	84	83	79	26	66
Chemistry	98	65	49	66	60	88	87	85	43	78

a) Represent the data with a scatter graph.

b) State the type of correlation, if any.

c) The students' science teacher thinks that the better a student is at physics, the better they'll be at chemistry. Do the exam results support this view?

d) Polly, a student in the class, made the following statement:
"The graph shows that being good at physics makes you better at chemistry."
Is it fair to say this from the data? Explain your answer.

Scatter Graphs and Bar Charts

Q4 10 people took 2 exams in Welding for Beginners. The table shows the marks obtained.

Candidate	1	2	3	4	5	6	7	8	9	10
Exam 1 (%)	85	30	55	10	40	20	0	95	65	40
Exam 2 (%)	70	25	50	15	70	25	5	80	60	35

a) Draw a scatter graph representing this information.

b) Identify any outliers by circling them on your graph. Draw a line of best fit.

c) Clive only sat the first exam, obtaining a mark of 50%. Use your scatter graph to estimate the mark that he might have achieved if he had sat the second exam.

Q5 Megan records whether people choose pizza or pasta in her Italian restaurant. The multiple bar chart below shows the results over one week.

a) On which days was pizza more popular with Megan's customers?

b) On which day did she have the most customers?

c) Why would a composite bar chart make it easier to answer part b)?

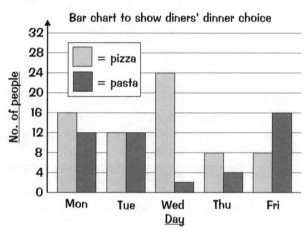

Q6 The graphs below show some statistics on marital status for people over 65 years old.

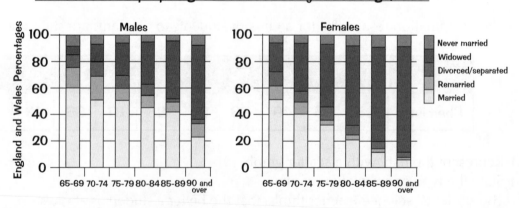

Marital status of people aged 65 and over: by sex and age, 2001

a) What proportion of males aged 65-69 are married?

b) What proportion of females aged 65-69 are married?

c) She also works out that the proportion of widowed males aged 90 and over is about 50% and for widowed females of the same age it's about 80%. Give one reason which would explain such a large difference.

Spread of Data

Q1 A dentist is about to employ a dental hygienist. She wishes to know if having a dental hygienist has an <u>effect on the number of fillings</u> she has to perform each year. So, prior to appointing him, the dentist takes some data from the record cards. Here it is:

No. of fillings	0	1	2	3	4	5
No. of children	1	2	8	30	60	12

<u>Three years after</u> appointing the dental hygienist, the dentist takes another set of data from the record cards. Here it is:

No. of fillings	0	1	2	3	4	5
No. of children	11	16	40	32	4	2

Using any statistical average you need, state what you see from the data, assuming that these records are for <u>new patients</u>.

Q2 The histograms below show the age distributions for two villages — **A** and **B**.

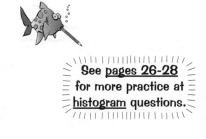

See pages <u>26-28</u> for more practice at <u>histogram</u> questions.

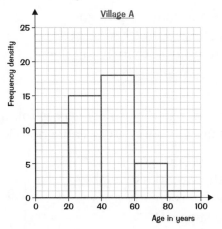

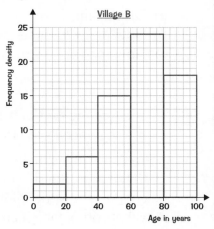

a) How many people in village **A** are between the ages of 20 and 40?
b) Which village has the larger population?
c) Make one comparison between the distribution of ages in village **A** and village **B**.

Q3 Match the histograms to their corresponding cumulative frequency curves.

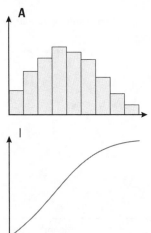

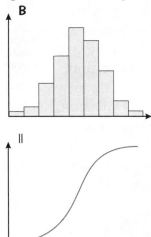

32

Other Graphs and Charts

Q1 One hundred vehicles on a road were recorded as part of a traffic study. Use this two-way table to answer the following questions.

	Van	Motor-bike	Car	Total
Travelling North	15			48
Travelling South	20		23	
Total		21		100

a) How many vans were recorded?
b) How many vehicles in the survey were travelling south?
c) How many motorbikes were travelling south?
d) How many cars were travelling north?

Q2 A sprinter is training for an athletics event. He has recorded the times of some of his training runs in the frequency table below.

Time (s)	$9 \leq t < 10$	$10 \leq t < 11$	$11 \leq t < 12$	$12 \leq t < 13$
Frequency	6	9	4	3

a) Display this information as a frequency polygon.
b) How many training runs has the sprinter recorded?
c) How many of his runs were quicker than 12 seconds?

Q3 The grading for skiers to be awarded certificates is as follows:
B - beginner, I - intermediate, G - good, VG - very good, R - racer.

To clarify the situation for a school group travelling to the Alps, the ski company would like a table and a chart to show the information as clearly as possible.

a) What sort of table can you suggest? Draw it accurately.
b) What sort of chart can you suggest? Draw it accurately.
c) What is the most common type of skier?

B	I	B	I	R	VG	I
I	R	G	VG	VG	B	B
I	I	B	B	R	B	G
I	B	G	G	I	I	I

Q4 Having seen the line graph opposite, a Quality Control Manager said "Admittedly we do have some complaints about our products, but from July complaints have tailed off, so our products must be of a better quality."
From the graph, do you think this statement is correct? Why/Why not?

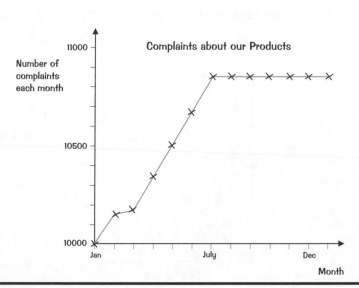

Other Graphs and Charts

Everyone loves a pie chart. Oh, no, sorry, that's pies...

When constructing a pie chart, follow the three steps:

1) Add up the numbers in each sector to get the <u>TOTAL</u>.
2) Divide 360° by the <u>TOTAL</u> to get the <u>MULTIPLIER</u>.
3) Multiply <u>EVERY</u> number by the <u>MULTIPLIER</u> to get the <u>ANGLE</u> of each <u>SECTOR</u>.

Q5 A company that makes and sells pies wants to add a nutritional information diagram to their packaging. <u>Construct a pie chart</u> using the template on the right, to show the following nutritional data for one of their pies:

Contents of Pie	Amount per 100 g
Carbohydrate	35 g
Protein	15 g
Fat	10 g
Magical fairy dust	40 g

Q6 According to the tourist board for the Hindle Isles, 380,000 people visited the biggest island in the group, Sherrington, in 2009. The <u>distribution</u> of tourists for the <u>whole group of islands</u> is shown in the pie chart. Use a <u>protractor</u> on the diagram to find the number of tourists visiting the other islands in 2009 (rounded to the nearest 10,000).

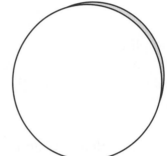

The distribution of visitors to the Hindle Isles in 2009

> Use the info you're given to find the number of tourists represented by 1°.

Q7 The pie chart shows the results of a survey of forty 11 year olds when asked what their <u>favourite vegetable</u> is with Sunday lunch. Which one of the following may be <u>deduced</u> from the information in the <u>pie chart</u>?

a) Potatoes are the <u>least popular</u> vegetable.
b) 3/4 of the children <u>like potatoes</u> of some type.
c) 1/10 of the children like <u>carrots or cauliflower</u>.
d) 11/40 of the children asked what their favourite vegetable is, replied "<u>Don't eat vegetables</u>."

Q8 The pie charts opposite appear in a newspaper article about a local election. Nicki says that more people voted for the Green party in 2009 than in 2005.

Comment on <u>whether it's possible</u> to tell this from the pie charts.

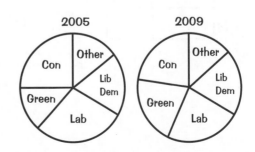

Basic Algebra

Q1   Work out the following temperature changes:

a) 20 °C to -7 °C

b) -10 °C to -32 °C

c) -17 °C to -5 °C

d) -3 °C to 15 °C

e) -31 °C to -16 °C

f) -5 °C to -17 °C

Q2   Which is larger and by how much?

a) $-12 + 7 - 4 + 6 - 2 + 7$ or **b)** $-30 + 26 - 3 - 7 + 17$

Q3   Simplify:

a) $4x - 5x + 3x - x + 2x - 7x$

b) $30y - 10y + 2y - 3y + 4y - 5y$

Q4   Find the value of xy and $\dfrac{x}{y}$ for each of the following:

a) $x = -100 \quad y = 10$

b) $x = 24 \qquad y = -4$

c) $x = -48 \quad y = -3$

d) $x = 0 \qquad y = -4$

Q5   Find the value of $(a - b) \div (c + d)$ when $a = 10$, $b = -26$, $c = -5$ and $d = -4$.

Q6   Simplify the following:

a) $2x \times -3y$

b) $-8a \times 2b$

c) $-4x \times -2x$

d) $4p \times -4p$

Q7   For each of the large rectangles below, write down the area of each of the small rectangles and hence find an expression for the area of each large rectangle.

a)

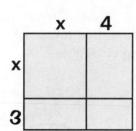

b)

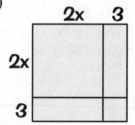

c)

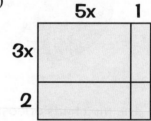

Eeeek — loads of questions...

Straight Line Graphs

Q1 ABCD is a <u>parallelogram</u>. A is (-1, 3), B is (-2,-1) and C is (4,-1).
Draw axes with *x* from -3 to 5 and *y* from -2 to 4.
Plot A, B and C then find the <u>missing coordinates</u> for D.

Q2 Draw axes with *x* from -9 to 9 and *y* from -12 to 12.
On the <u>same</u> set of axes draw the following shapes and find their
<u>missing pair of coordinates</u>.

a) ABCD is a <u>square</u>
A is (1, 1)
B is ?
C is (-3,-3)
D is (-3, 1)

c) ABCD is a <u>rectangle</u>
A is ?
B is (3,-8)
C is (3,-6)
D is (-5,-6)

e) ABCD is a <u>parallelogram</u>
A is (-2,-10)
B is (4,-10)
C is (6,-12)
D is ?

b) ABCD is a <u>parallelogram</u>
A is (2, 8)
B is (6, 8)
C is ?
D is (1, 5)

d) ABCD is a <u>kite</u>
A is (-9, 3)
B is (-6, 8)
C is (-4, 8)
D is ?

f) ABCD is a <u>parallelogram</u>
A is (-8, 10)
B is (-6, 10)
C is ?
D is (-5, 12)

Q3 Which letters represent the following lines:

a) $x = y$
b) $x = 5$
c) $y = -x$
d) $x = 0$
e) $y = -7$
f) $x + y = 0$
g) $y = 5$
h) $x - y = 0$
i) $y = 0$
j) $x = -7$?

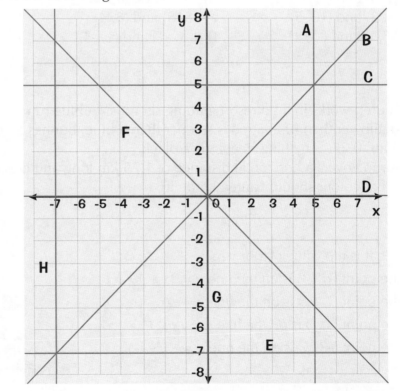

Don't get confused if you've got "x + y = ... " — just rearrange the equation
to "y = -x + ..." and as if by magic, you've got a line you recognise.

Straight Line Graphs

Q4 What is the gradient of:

a) line A

b) line B

c) line C

d) line D

e) line E

f) line F

g) line G

h) line H

i) line I

j) line J

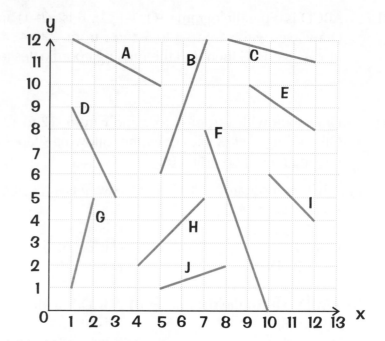

Uphill gradients are always positive, downhill always negative. Impressed?
Hmmm....thought not. Can be a bit of an uphill battle, these.

Q5 What is the gradient of the lines joining the points:

a) (3, 5) and (5, 9)

b) (6, 3) and (10, 5)

c) (-6, 4) and (-3, 1)

d) (8, 2) and (4, 10)

e) (8, 5) and (6, 4)

f) (-3, -1) and (1, -4)?

Q6 Lauren works in a ski resort grading ski runs. A blue run has a gradient shallower than -0.2, a red is steeper than a blue, but has a gradient shallower than -0.25. Anything steeper is a black.
A run covers a horizontal distance of 1.75 km long and descends 400 meters. What colour should Lauren grade it?

Q7 What is the value of x or y if:

a) the point $(x, 13)$ is on the line $y = 3x + 1$

b) the point $(x, -2)$ is on the line $y = \frac{1}{2}x - 6$

c) the point $(4, y)$ is on the line $y = 2x - 1$

d) the point $(-3, y)$ is on the line $y = -3x$?

Q8 Which of the following points lie on the line $y = 3x - 1$?
(7, 20), (6, 15), (5, 14)

Straight Line Graphs

If you know it's a straight line, you only really need <u>two</u> points, but it's always a <u>good idea</u> to plot three — it's a bit of a safety net, really.

Q9 Complete this table of values for $y = 2x + 3$:

X	0	3	8
y			

Plot these points on graph paper and draw the graph of $y = 2x + 3$.
Use your graph to find:

a) The value of y when $x = 5$
b) The value of y when $x = 2$
c) The value of x when $y = 11$
d) The value of x when $y = 17$

Q10 Complete this table of values for $y = \frac{1}{4}x - 3$:

X	-8	-4	8
y			

Plot these points on graph paper and draw the graph of $y = \frac{1}{4}x - 3$.
Use your graph to find:

a) The value of y when $x = 2$
b) The value of y when $x = 0$
c) The value of x when $y = -2$
d) The value of x when $y = -1.5$

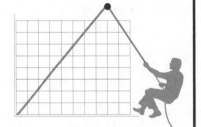

Q11 The cost of electricity is calculated using the formula:
Total cost = Fixed charge + (cost per unit × number of units).
Customers can choose two different methods of payment:
Method A: Fixed charge £10, cost per unit 25p
Method B: Fixed charge £40, cost per unit 5p
Copy and complete this table:

Number of Units used	0	100	200	300
Cost using method A				
Cost using method B				

Plot these points on a graph (put the number of units on the horizontal axis, cost on the vertical axis):

a) Use your graph to find the total cost when 70 units are used for:
   i) Method A
   ii) Method B

b) Miss Wright used 75 units. Which method should she use to minimize her bill, Method A or Method B?

c) Use your graph to work out how many units Miss Wright would have to use for both methods to cost the same amount.

38

Real-Life Graphs

Q1 This graph can be used to convert the distance (miles) travelled in a taxi to the fare payable (£). How much will the fare be if you travel:

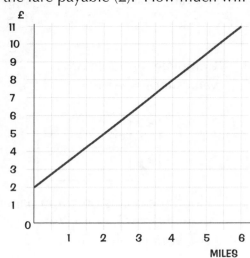

a) 2 miles

b) 5 miles

c) 10 miles

d) Mike lives 4.5 miles away from his friend. Is £16 enough money for Mike to get a taxi to his friend's house and back?

Q2 80 km is roughly equal to 50 miles. Use this information to draw a conversion graph. Use the graph to estimate the number of miles equal to:

a) 20 km
b) 70 km
c) 90 km

When you've got to draw your own conversion graph, your best bet is to work out a few different values, and mark them on the graph first.

Q3 How many km are equal to:

a) 40 miles
b) 10 miles
c) 30 miles

Q4 In her science lesson, Ellie pours water into different shaped containers at a <u>constant rate</u>, then plots graphs of the <u>depth</u> of water (*d*) against <u>time</u> (*t*) taken to fill the container.

At the end of the lesson she realises she hasn't labelled her graphs. Which graph matches each container? Write in the letters below.

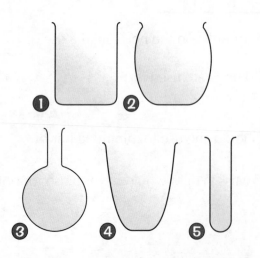

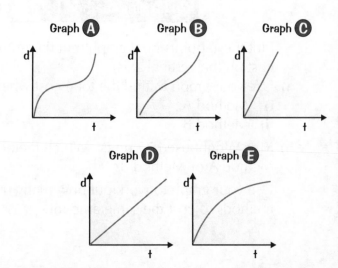

Types of Number

There are a few special number sequences that you really need to know — SQUARE, CUBE, TRIANGULAR and PRIME NUMBERS, as well as POWERS and ODD and EVEN NUMBERS.

Q1 Sarah thinks of a number. She calculates that the square of the number is 256. What is the square root of the number?

Q2 On a certain day the temperature at midday was 14°C. By midnight the temperature had fallen by 17°C. What was the temperature at midnight?

Q3 1 is the first odd number. It is also the first square number and the first cube number. Which is greater:
a) the third odd number, the third square number or the third cube number?
b) the sixth odd number, the fourth square number or the second cube number?

Q4 The following sequences are described in words. Write down their first four terms.
a) The prime numbers starting from 17.
b) The squares of odd numbers starting from $9^2 = 81$.

Q5 Using any or all of the figures **1, 2, 5, 9** write down:
a) the smallest prime number
b) a prime number greater than 20
c) a prime number between 10 and 20
d) two prime numbers whose sum is 21
e) a number that is not prime.

> Remember — 1 is not a prime.
> Look, it just isn't, OK.

Q6 a) In the ten by ten square opposite, ring all the <u>prime numbers</u>. (The first three have been done for you.)
b) Among the prime numbers between 10 and 100, find three which are still prime when their digits are reversed.
c) Give a reason for 27 not being a prime number.

1	②	③	4	⑤	6	7	8	9	10
11	12	13	14	15	16	17	18	19	20
21	22	23	24	25	26	27	28	29	30
31	32	33	34	35	36	37	38	39	40
41	42	43	44	45	46	47	48	49	50
51	52	53	54	55	56	57	58	59	60
61	62	63	64	65	66	67	68	69	70
71	72	73	74	75	76	77	78	79	80
81	82	83	84	85	86	87	88	89	90
91	92	93	94	95	96	97	98	99	100

Q7 What is the largest prime less than 120?

Q8 How many prime numbers are even?

Multiples, Factors and Prime Factors

Q1   1   3   6   9   12
From the numbers above, write down:

a) a multiple of 4
b) the prime number
c) two square numbers
d) three factors of 27
e) two numbers, P and Q, that satisfy both $P = 2Q$ and $P = \sqrt{144}$

This is real basic stuff —
you just have to know
your times tables. And
your primes, of course...

Q2   48 students went on a geography field trip
Their teachers split them into equal groups
Suggest five different ways that the teachers
might have split up the students.

Q3   A school ran 3 evening classes: Conversational French, Cake Making and Woodturning.
The Conversational French class had 29 students, Cake Making had 27 students, and the
Woodturning class had 23. For which classes did the teacher have difficulty dividing the
students into equal groups?

Q4   a) Write down the first five cube numbers.
   b) Which of the numbers given in part **a)** are multiples of 2?
   c) Which of the numbers given in part **a)** are multiples of 3?
   d) Which of the numbers given in part **a)** are multiples of 4?
   e) Which of the numbers given in part **a)** are multiples of 5?

Q5   Write down the prime factorisation of:
   a) 18
   b) 140
   c) 47

The tricky bit is remembering that a <u>prime factorisation</u>
includes <u>all</u> the prime factors that multiply to make that
number — so you've got to repeat some of them.

Q6   a) List the first five prime numbers.
   b) If added together, what is their total?
   c) Write down the prime factorisation of the answer to part **b)**.

Q7   a) List the first five odd numbers.
   b) If added together, what is their total?
   c) Write down the prime factorisation of the answer to part **b)**.

Multiples, Factors and Prime Factors

Q8 The prime factorisation of a certain number is $3^2 \times 5 \times 11$.
  a) Write down the number.
  b) Write down the prime factorisation of 165.

Q9 The first ten numbers in a sequence are: 1, 3, 6, 10, 15, 21, 28, 36, 45, 55.
  a) From the list pick out all the multiples of 2.
  b) From the list pick out all the multiples of 3.
  c) From the list pick out any prime numbers.
  d) Add the numbers in the list together and
    write down the prime factorisation of the total.

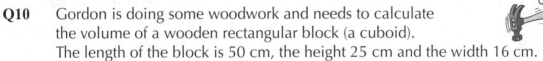

Q10 Gordon is doing some woodwork and needs to calculate
    the volume of a wooden rectangular block (a cuboid).
    The length of the block is 50 cm, the height 25 cm and the width 16 cm.
  a) What is the volume (in cm³) of the wooden block?
  b) What is the prime factorisation of the number found in part **a)**?
  c) Gordon needs to cut the block into smaller blocks with dimensions 4 cm × 5 cm × 5 cm.
    What is the maximum number of small blocks Gordon can make from the larger block?
    Make sure you show all your working.

Q11 The prime factorisation of a certain number is $2^3 \times 5 \times 17$.
  a) What is the number?
  b) What is the prime factorisation of half of this number?
  c) What is the prime factorisation of a quarter of the number?
  d) What is the prime factorisation of an eighth of the number?

Q12 Bryan and Sue were playing a guessing game. Sue thought of a number
    between 1 and 100 which Bryan had to guess. Bryan was allowed to ask five
    questions, which are listed with Sue's responses in the table below.

Bryan's Questions	Sue's Responses
Is it prime?	No
Is it odd?	No
Is it less than 50?	Yes
Is it a multiple of 3?	Yes
Is it a multiple of 7?	Yes

Start by writing down
a number table up to 100.
Look at each response in
turn and cross off numbers
'till you've only got
one left.

What is the number that Sue thought of?

LCM and HCF

Top tip These two fancy names always put people off — but really they're dead easy. Just learn these simple facts:

1) The Lowest Common Multiple (LCM) is the SMALLEST number that will DIVIDE BY ALL the numbers in question.

E.g. 3, 6, 9, 12, 15 are all multiples of 3.
5, 10, 15, 20, 25 are all multiples of 5.
The lowest number that is in both lists is 15, so 15 is the LCM of 3 and 5.

2) The Highest Common Factor (HCF) is the BIGGEST number that will DIVIDE INTO ALL the numbers in question.

E.g. 1, 2, 4, 8 are all factors of 8.
1, 2, 3, 4, 6, 12 are all factors of 12.
The highest number that is in both lists is 4, so 4 is the HCF of 8 and 12.

Q1 **a)** List the first ten multiples of 6, starting at 6.
b) List the first ten multiples of 5, starting at 5.
c) What is the LCM of 5 and 6?

I tell you what, it's a lot easier to find the LCM or HCF once you've listed the multiples or factors. If you miss out this step it'll all go horribly wrong, believe me.

Q2 **a)** List all the factors of 30.
b) List all the factors of 48.
c) What is the HCF of 30 and 48?

Q3 For each set of numbers find the HCF.
a) 40, 60   **d)** 15, 45   **g)** 32, 64
b) 10, 40, 60   **e)** 15, 30, 45   **h)** 32, 48, 64
c) 10, 24, 40, 60   **f)** 15, 20, 30, 45   **i)** 16, 32, 48, 64

Q4 For each set of numbers find the LCM.
a) 40, 60   **d)** 15, 45   **g)** 32, 64
b) 10, 40, 60   **e)** 15, 30, 45   **h)** 32, 48, 64
c) 10, 24, 40, 60   **f)** 15, 20, 30, 45   **i)** 16, 32, 48, 64

Q5 Lars, Rita and Alan regularly go swimming. Lars goes every 2 days, Rita goes every 3 days and Alan goes every 5 days. They all went swimming together on Friday 1st June.

This is just a LCM question in disguise.

a) On what date will Lars and Rita next go swimming together?
b) On what date will Rita and Alan next go swimming together?
c) On what day of the week will all 3 next go swimming together?
d) Which of the 3 (if any) will go swimming on 15th June?

Powers and Roots

 Hang on there. Before you try this page, make sure you know all the rules for dealing with powers...

Q1 Complete the following:
a) $2^4 = 2 \times 2 \times 2 \times 2$ =
b) $10^3 = 10 \times 10 \times 10$ =
c) $3^5 = 3 \times ...$ =
d) $4^6 = 4 \times ...$ =
e) $1^9 = 1 \times ...$ =
f) $5^6 = 5 \times ...$ =

Q2 Simplify the following:
a) $2 \times 2 \times 2 \times 2 \times 2 \times 2 \times 2 \times 2$
b) $12 \times 12 \times 12 \times 12 \times 12$
c) $x \times x \times x \times x \times x \times x \times x$
d) $m \times m \times m$
e) $y \times y \times y \times y$
f) $z \times z \times z \times z \times z \times z$

Q3 Complete the following (the first one has been done for you):
a) $10^2 \times 10^3 = (10 \times 10) \times (10 \times 10 \times 10) = 10^5$
b) $10^3 \times 10^4 =$ =
c) $10^4 \times 10^2 =$ =
d) $10^5 \times 10^3 =$ =
e) What is the <u>quick method</u> for writing down the final result in **b)**, **c)** and **d)**?

Easy — you'll have learnt this from your power rules.

Q4 Complete the following (the first one has been done for you):
a) $2^4 \div 2^2 = \dfrac{(2 \times 2 \times 2 \times 2)}{(2 \times 2)} = 2^2$
c) $4^5 \div 4^3 = \dfrac{(4 \times 4 \times 4 \times 4 \times 4)}{} =$
b) $2^5 \div 2^2 = \dfrac{(2 \times 2 \times 2 \times 2 \times 2)}{(2 \times 2)} =$
d) $8^5 \div 8^2 =$ =

e) What is the quick method for writing down the final result in **b)**, **c)** and **d)**?

Q5 Which of the following are <u>true</u>?
a) $2^4 \times 2^6 = 2^{10}$
b) $2^2 \times 2^3 \times 2^4 = 2^9$
c) $2^3 \times 2^2 = 2^6$
d) $4^{10} \times 4^4 \times 4^2 = 4^{18}$
e) $2^1 \times 2^3 \times 2^4 = 2^8$
f) $10^4 \times 10^2 = 10^8$
g) $2^{20} \div 2^5 = 2^4$
h) $3^{12} \div 3^4 = 3^8$
i) $4^6 \div 6^4 = 4^2$
j) $10^{20} \div 10^3 = 10^{17}$
k) $4^6 \div (4^2 \times 4^3) = 4^1$
l) $9^2 \times (9^{30} \div 9^{25}) = 9^{10}$

Q6 Remove the brackets from the following and express as a single power:
a) $(3^4 \times 3^2) \div (3^6 \times 3^3)$
b) $(4^{10} \times 4^{12}) \times 4^3$
c) $10^2 \div (10^3 \times 10^{12})$
d) $(3^6)^{-2}$
e) $4^2 \times 4^{-1} \times 4^6 \times (4^2 \div 4^3)$
f) $(5^2 \times 5^3) \div (5^6 \div 5^4)$

Powers and Roots

Q7   Without using a calculator, write down both answers to each of the following:

a) $\sqrt{4} =$ e) $\sqrt{36} =$ i) $\sqrt{144} =$

b) $\sqrt{16} =$ f) $\sqrt{49} =$ j) $\sqrt{64} =$

c) $\sqrt{9} =$ g) $\sqrt{25} =$ k) $\sqrt{81} =$

d) $\sqrt{1} =$ h) $\sqrt{100} =$ l) $\sqrt{121} =$

Q8   Without using a calculator, find the value of the following:

a) $\sqrt[3]{64}$ e) $\sqrt[3]{27}$

b) $\sqrt[3]{512}$ f) $\sqrt[3]{1000}$

c) $\sqrt[3]{125}$ g) $\sqrt[3]{216}$

d) $\sqrt[3]{8}$ h) $\sqrt[3]{8000}$

Q9   A square lawn has an area of 400 m².
What is the length of an edge?

Q10   Nida is buying a small gift box online. She sees a cube box with volume
of 125 cm³. What is the length of each box edge?

Q11   A farmer is buying fencing to surround a square field of area 3600 m².
What length of fencing does he need to buy?

Q12   Without using a calculator, find the value of the following:

a) $(6.5)^3$ e) $(2.25)^1$ i) $121^{\frac{1}{2}}$

b) $(0.35)^2$ f) 5^{-3} j) $8^{\frac{1}{3}}$

c) $(0.04)^0$ g) 2^{-2} k) $216^{-\frac{1}{3}}$

d) $(1\frac{1}{2})^2$ h) $(1.5)^{-1}$ l) $8^{\frac{2}{3}}$

Remember — fractional powers mean roots.

Standard Index Form

Writing very big (or very small) numbers gets a bit messy with all those zeros if you don't use this standard index form. But of course, the main reason for knowing about standard form is... you guessed it — it's in the Exam.

Q1 Delilah is doing some calculations for her science homework.
She needs to give her answers as ordinary numbers.
How should she write the following answers?

a) 3.56×10
b) 3.56×10^3
c) 3.56×10^{-1}
d) 3.56×10^4

e) 0.082×10^2
f) 0.082×10^{-2}
g) 0.082×10
h) 0.082×10^{-1}

i) 157×10
j) 157×10^{-3}
k) 157×10^3
l) 157×10^{-1}

Q2 Write in standard form:

a) 2.56
b) 25.6
c) 0.256
d) 25 600

e) 95.2
f) 0.0952
g) 95 200
h) 0.000952

i) 4200
j) 0.0042
k) 42
l) 420.

Q3 Write in standard form:

a) 34.7×10
b) 73.004
c) 0.005×10^3
d) 9183×10^2

e) 15 million
f) 937.1×10^4
g) 0.000075
h) 0.05×10^{-2}

i) 534×10^{-2}
j) 621.03
k) 149×10^2
l) 0.003×10^{-4}.

When scientists write about massive things such as the universe, or tiny things such as cells and particles, it's often more convenient to write numbers in standard form. Write the numbers in Questions 4 to 7 in standard form.

Q4 The average diameter of a cell nucleus in a mammal is around 0.006 mm.

Q5 A billion = a thousand million   A trillion = a thousand billion.

Q6 A light year is 9 460 000 000 000 km (approx).

Q7 Nautilus covered 69 138 miles before having to refuel.

Q8 A tissue sample is three cells thick. Each cell has a thickness of 0.000004 m. What is the thickness of the tissue sample, in mm? Give your answer in standard form.

Q9 This table gives the diameter and distance from the Sun of some planets.

Planet	Distance from Sun (km)	Diameter (km)
Earth	1.5×10^8	1.3×10^4
Venus	1.085×10^8	1.2×10^4
Mars	2.28×10^8	6.8×10^3
Mercury	5.81×10^7	4.9×10^3
Jupiter	7.8×10^8	1.4×10^5
Neptune	4.52×10^9	4.9×10^4
Saturn	1.43×10^9	1.2×10^5

From the table write down which planet is:
a) smallest in diameter
b) largest in diameter
c) nearest to the Sun
d) furthest from the Sun.

Write down which planets are:
e) nearer to the Sun than the Earth
f) bigger in diameter than the Earth.

Fractions and Decimals

Answer the following questions without using a calculator.

Q1 Carry out the following multiplications, giving your answers in their lowest terms:

a) $\dfrac{2}{3} \times \dfrac{1}{6}$ b) $1\dfrac{1}{4} \times 3\dfrac{1}{8}$ c) $\dfrac{9}{10} \times \dfrac{9}{100} \times \dfrac{1}{100}$

Q2 Carry out the following divisions, giving your answers in their lowest terms:

a) $\dfrac{2}{3} \div \dfrac{1}{6}$ b) $1\dfrac{1}{4} \div 3\dfrac{1}{8}$ c) $\left(\dfrac{9}{10} \div \dfrac{9}{100}\right) \div \dfrac{1}{100}$

Q3 Evaluate the following, giving your answers in their lowest terms:

a) $\dfrac{1}{6} + \dfrac{2}{3}$ b) $1\dfrac{1}{4} + 3\dfrac{1}{8}$ c) $\dfrac{9}{10} + \dfrac{9}{100} + \dfrac{1}{100}$

Q4 Caley is making some punch for her birthday party. She mixes $\dfrac{1}{2}$ litre of cranberry juice, $1\dfrac{1}{2}$ litres of apple juice, $\dfrac{2}{3}$ litre of orange juice and $\dfrac{4}{5}$ litres of pineapple juice.
She has a bowl that will hold 4 litres. Will this be big enough to contain all of the punch?

Q5 Evaluate the following, giving your answers in their lowest terms:

a) $\dfrac{2}{3} - \dfrac{1}{6}$ b) $3\dfrac{1}{8} - 1\dfrac{1}{4}$ c) $\left(\dfrac{9}{10} - \dfrac{9}{100}\right) - \dfrac{1}{100}$

Q6 Evaluate the following, giving your answers in their lowest terms:

a) $\dfrac{1}{2} + \dfrac{1}{4}$ d) $6 \times \dfrac{2}{3}$ g) $\dfrac{2}{3}\left(\dfrac{3}{4} + \dfrac{4}{5}\right)$

b) $\dfrac{2}{3} - \dfrac{1}{4}$ e) $\dfrac{4}{5} \div \dfrac{2}{3}$ h) $\left(\dfrac{1}{7} + \dfrac{3}{14}\right) \times \left(3 - \dfrac{1}{5}\right)$

c) $\dfrac{1}{5} + \dfrac{2}{3} - \dfrac{2}{5}$ f) $\dfrac{5}{6} - \dfrac{7}{8}$ i) $\left(\dfrac{3}{4} - \dfrac{1}{5}\right) \div \left(\dfrac{7}{8} + \dfrac{1}{16}\right)$

Q7 Write the following fractions as recurring decimals:

a) $\dfrac{10}{11}$ b) $\dfrac{29}{63}$ c) $\dfrac{478}{999}$ d) $\dfrac{5891}{9999}$

Q8 Write the following decimals as fractions in their lowest form:

a) 0.6   b) 0.75   c) 0.95   d) 0.128

e) $0.\dot{3}$ f) $0.\dot{6}$ g) $0.\dot{1}$ h) $0.\overline{16}$

Q9 Write the following recurring decimals as fractions in their lowest form:

a) 0.222...   b) 0.444...   c) 0.888...   d) 0.808080...

e) 0.121212...   f) 0.545545545...   g) 0.753753753...   h) 0.156156156...

Fractions and Decimals

The cunning bit with long wordy questions is picking out the important bits and then translating them into numbers. It's not that easy at first, but you'll get better — I guess you've just gotta learn to ignore the waffly stuff.

Answer these without using your calculator:

Q10 What fraction of 1 hour is:
a) 5 minutes
b) 15 minutes
c) 40 minutes?

Q11 If a TV programme lasts 40 minutes, what fraction of the programme is left after:
a) 10 minutes
b) 15 minutes
c) 35 minutes?

Q12 A café employs eighteen girls and twelve boys to wait at tables. Another six boys and nine girls work in the kitchen.
What fraction of the <u>kitchen staff</u> are girls?
What fraction of the <u>employees</u> are boys?

Q13

In a survey, people were asked if they liked a new cola drink. One in five thought it was great, four out of fifteen felt there was no difference in taste, three in ten disliked it and <u>the rest</u> offered no opinion.
What fraction of people offered no opinion?

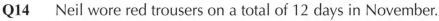

Forget all about cola drinks and red trousers — just write it all as a sum, then do the calculation. Nowt to it.

Q14 Neil wore red trousers on a total of 12 days in November.
a) On what fraction of the total number of days in November did Neil wear <u>red trousers</u>?
b) For 1/5 of the days in November Neil wore a <u>blue shirt</u>. How many days is this?

Q15

The Sandwich Club of Great Britain are going on their annual picnic.
a) The boxes they use to transport their sandwiches are 10 inches high and are the width of a single sandwich. Each sandwich is 5/8 inch thick. How many boxes will they need for 80 sandwiches?
b) How tall would the box need to be if <u>40</u> sandwiches were to be stacked inside?

Manipulating Surds and Use of π

Well, to be honest, I think the idea of rational and irrational numbers is a bit odd.
Basically, you can write a <u>rational</u> number as a <u>whole</u> number or a <u>fraction</u>.
An <u>irrational</u> number... you guessed it... is <u>not</u> whole and <u>can't</u> be written as a fraction.

Q1 If $x = 2$, $y = \sqrt{3}$ and $z = 2\sqrt{2}$, which of the following expressions are rational and which are irrational? Show your working.

a) xyz

b) $(xyz)^2$

c) $x + yz$

d) $\dfrac{yz}{2\sqrt{3x}}$

Q2 A circle has a radius of $\sqrt{3}$ cm. What is its exact area? (Area of circle = πr^2.)

Q3 Simplify:

> Remember — $\sqrt{a} \times \sqrt{b} = \sqrt{(ab)}$.

a) $\sqrt{5} \times \sqrt{3}$

b) $\dfrac{\sqrt{20}}{\sqrt{5}}$

c) $\sqrt{4} - \sqrt{1}$

d) $\left(\dfrac{\sqrt{5}}{\sqrt{2}}\right)^2$

e) $\left(\sqrt{x}\right)^2$

f) $\sqrt{x^2}$

g) $\sqrt{8} \times \sqrt{8}$

h) $\sqrt{18} - \sqrt{9}$

Q4 Are the following expressions rational or irrational?

a) $(1+\sqrt{5})(1-\sqrt{5})$

b) $\dfrac{1 + \sqrt{5}}{1 - \sqrt{5}}$

Q5 If $x = 1$ and $y = \sqrt{2}$, are the following expressions rational or irrational?

a) $(x + y)(x - y)$

b) $\dfrac{x + y}{x - y}$

Q6 Rationalise the denominators of the following expressions, and then simplify if necessary.

a) $\dfrac{1}{\sqrt{2}}$

b) $\dfrac{2}{\sqrt{8}}$

c) $\dfrac{a}{\frac{\sqrt{40}}{2}}$

d) $\dfrac{x}{\sqrt{xy}}$

e) $\dfrac{1}{1 + \sqrt{2}}$

f) $\dfrac{6}{3 + \sqrt{3}}$

g) $\dfrac{2}{1 + \sqrt{6}}$

h) $\dfrac{5 + \sqrt{5}}{5 - \sqrt{5}}$

> Remember: rationalising the denominator means getting rid of the square root signs on the bottom of fractions.

More Algebra

Q1 Simplify the following by collecting like terms together:

a) $3x^2 + 4x + 12x^2 - 5x$

b) $12 - 4x^2 + 10x - 3x^2 + 2x$

c) $20abc + 12ab + 10bac + 4b$

d) $4pq - 14p - 8q + p - q + 8p$

e) $13x^2 + 4x^2 - 5y^2 + y^2 - x^2$

f) $3x^2 + 4xy + 2y^2 - z^2 + 2xy - y^2 - 5x^2$

Q2 Multiply out the brackets and simplify where possible:

a) $4(x + y - z)$

b) $-3(x - 2)$

c) $7(a + b) + 2(a + b)$

d) $4(x - 2) - 2(x - 1)$

e) $4e(e + 2f) + 2f(e - f)$

f) $4x(x + 2) - 2x(3 - x)$

g) $3(2 + ab) + 5(1 - ab)$

h) $4(x - 2y) - (5 + x - 2y)$

i) $x^2(x + 1)$

j) $4x^2\left(x + 2 + \dfrac{1}{x}\right)$

k) $7pq\left(p + q - \dfrac{1}{p}\right)$

Q3 Multiply out the brackets and simplify your answers where possible:

a) $(x - 3)(x + 1)$

b) $(x + 10)(x + 3)$

c) $(x - 5)(x - 2)$

d) $(x + 2)(x - 7)$

e) $(2 + 3x)(3x - 1)$

f) $(3x + 2)(2x - 4)$

g) $(x - 3)(4x + 1)$

h) $4(x + 2y)(3x - 2y)$

i) $(3x + 2y)^2$

Q4 Find the product of $5x - 2$ and $3x + 2$.

Q5 Find the square of $2x - 1$.

Q6 A rectangular pond has length $(3x - 2)$ m and width $(5 - x)$ m.
Write down a simplified expression for:

a) the pond's perimeter

b) the pond's area.

Q7 A rectangular bar of chocolate consists of 20 small rectangular pieces. The size of a small rectangular piece of chocolate is 2 cm by x cm.

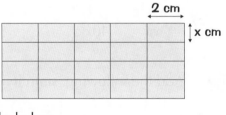

a) Write down an expression for the perimeter of the whole bar.

b) Write down an expression for the area of the whole bar.

c) If I ate 6 small rectangular pieces of chocolate, what is the area of the remaining bar?

Q8 Find a simplified expression for the perimeter *and* the area of the following shapes.

a)

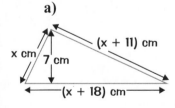

b)

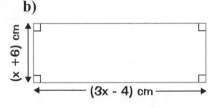

c)

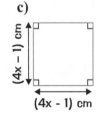

d)

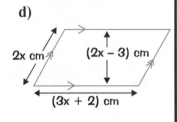

Q9 All the expressions below have a^2 as a common factor. Factorise each of them.

a) $a^2b + a^2c$

b) $5a^2 + 13a^2b$

c) $2a^2b + 3a^2c$

d) $a^3 + a^2y$

e) $2a^2x + 3a^2y + 4a^2z$

f) $a^2b^2 + a^3c^2$

Q10 Factorise and simplify the following:

a) $4xyz + 8xyz$

b) $8xyz + 12xyz$

c) $8xyz + 16 x^2yz$

d) $20 x^2y^2z^2 + 16 xyz^2$

More Algebra

Q11 Using the fact that $a^2 - b^2 = (a + b)(a - b)$, factorise the following expressions:
a) $x^2 - 9$
c) $36 - a^2$
e) $25 - 16z^2$
g) $1 - (ab)^2$
b) $25 - z^2$
d) $9y^2 - 4$
f) $x^4 - 36$
h) $100\,x^2 - 144y^2$

Q12 Factorise:
a) $x^2 - 4$
b) $144 - y^4$
c) $1 - 9x^2y^2$
d) $49x^4y^4 - 1$

Q13 Simplify the following by cancelling down where possible:
a) $\dfrac{27x^4y^2z}{9x^3yz^2}$
b) $\dfrac{48a^2b^2}{(2a)^2c}$
c) $\dfrac{3xyz}{9x^2y^3z^4}$
d) $\dfrac{4p^3q^3}{(2pr)^3}$

Q14 Multiply out the following, leaving your answers as simplified as possible:
a) $\dfrac{2x}{y^2} \times \dfrac{y^3}{4x^3}$
b) $\dfrac{10z^3}{xy} \times \dfrac{4x^3}{5z}$
c) $\dfrac{30a^2b^2c^2}{7} \times \dfrac{21c^2}{ab^3}$
d) $\dfrac{400d^4}{51e^5} \times \dfrac{102d^2e^4}{800e^2f}$

Q15 Divide the following, leaving your answer as simplified as possible:
a) $\dfrac{30x^3}{y^2} \div \dfrac{10x}{y}$
b) $\dfrac{e^2f^2}{5} \div \dfrac{ef}{10}$
c) $\dfrac{70f^3}{g} \div \dfrac{10f^4}{g^2}$

It helps if you can cancel some factors before multiplying.

Q16 Solve the following equations for x:
a) $\dfrac{20x^4y^2z^3}{7xy^5} \times \dfrac{14y^3}{40x^2z^3} = 5$
b) $\dfrac{48x^5y^2}{12z^3} \div \dfrac{16x^2y^2}{z^3} = 2$

Q17 Add the following, simplifying your answers:
a) $\dfrac{3}{2x} + \dfrac{y}{2x}$
b) $\dfrac{(4x + 2)}{3} + \dfrac{(2x - 1)}{3}$
c) $\dfrac{x}{10} + \dfrac{y - 1}{5}$
d) $\dfrac{zx}{4} + \dfrac{x + z}{y}$

Q18 Subtract the following, leaving your answers as simplified as possible:
a) $\dfrac{(9 - 5x)}{3x} - \dfrac{(3 + x)}{3x}$
b) $\dfrac{10 + x^2}{4x} - \dfrac{x^2 + 11}{4x}$
c) $\dfrac{(p + q)}{2} - \dfrac{3p}{5}$
d) $\dfrac{p - 2q}{4} - \dfrac{2p + q}{2}$

Q19 Simplify the following:
a) $\left(\dfrac{a}{b} \div \dfrac{c}{d}\right) \times \dfrac{ac}{bd}$
c) $\dfrac{m^2n}{p} + \dfrac{mn}{p^2}$
e) $\dfrac{1}{4pq} \div \dfrac{1}{3pq}$
b) $\dfrac{(p + q)}{r} \times \dfrac{3}{2(p + q)}$
d) $\dfrac{2}{x} - \dfrac{3}{2x} + \dfrac{4}{3x}$
f) $\dfrac{x}{8} - \dfrac{x + y}{4} + \dfrac{x - y}{2}$

Factorising Quadratics

Q1 Factorise the quadratics first, and then solve the equations:

a) $x^2 + 3x - 10 = 0$ **d)** $x^2 - 4x + 3 = 0$ **g)** $x^2 + 6x - 7 = 0$
b) $x^2 - 5x + 6 = 0$ **e)** $x^2 - x - 20 = 0$ **h)** $x^2 + 14x + 49 = 0$
c) $x^2 - 2x + 1 = 0$ **f)** $x^2 - 4x - 5 = 0$ **i)** $x^2 - 2x - 15 = 0.$

Q2 Rearrange into the form "$x^2 + bx + c = 0$", then solve by factorising:

a) $x^2 + 6x = 16$ **f)** $x^2 - 21 = 4x$ **k)** $x + 4 - \dfrac{21}{x} = 0$

b) $x^2 + 5x = 36$ **g)** $x^2 - 300 = 20x$ **l)** $x(x - 3) = 10$

c) $x^2 + 4x = 45$ **h)** $x^2 + 48 = 26x$ **m)** $x^2 - 3(x + 6) = 0$

d) $x^2 = 5x$ **i)** $x^2 + 36 = 13x$ **n)** $x - \dfrac{63}{x} = 2$

e) $x^2 = 11x$ **j)** $x + 5 - \dfrac{14}{x} = 0$ **o)** $x + 1 = \dfrac{12}{x}$

Q3 Solve $x^2 - \dfrac{1}{4} = 0.$

Q4 The area of a rectangular swimming pool is 28 m². The width is x m. The difference between the length and width is 3 m. Find the value of x.

Q5 A rug has length x m. The width is exactly 1 m less than the length.

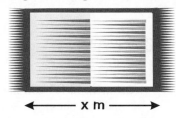

a) Write down an expression for the area of the rug.
b) If the area of the rug is 6 m², find the value of x.

Q6 A triangle has height $(x + 1)$ cm and a base of $2x$ cm.

a) Write down an expression for the area of the triangle and simplify it.
b) If the area of the triangle is 12 cm², find the value of x.

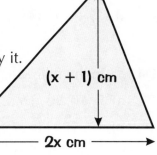

Q7 A square room has a floor of sides x metres. The height of the walls is 3 m. Write down an expression for:
a) the floor area
b) the area of all four walls.
c) If the total area of the floor and the four walls is 64 m², form a quadratic equation and solve it to find x.

Sequences

There are four special sequences: EVEN, ODD, SQUARE and CUBE. You really need to know them and their nth terms.

Q1 Write down the next 3 terms in each of these sequences and describe the sequence.

a) 2, 4, 6, 8, ...

b) 1, 3, 5, 7, ...

c) 1, 4, 9, 16, ...

d) 1, 8, 27, 64, ...

They're bound to ask you to <u>find the nth term</u> in the exam, so make sure you learn the <u>formula</u>.

Q2   **6   11   16   21   26 ...**

a) What are the next 3 terms in this sequence?

b) What is the difference between each term?

c) Write down a formula for the nth term of this sequence.

d) Use the formula to find the 20th term of the sequence.

Q3 Write down an expression for the nth term of the following sequences:

a) 2, 4, 6, 8, …

b) 1, 3, 5, 7, …

c) 5, 10, 15, 20, …

d) 5, 8, 11, 14, …

OK then, I'll tell you the formula just this once: $dn + (a - d)$
(d = difference, a = 1st term)
<u>**LEARN IT!**</u>

Q4 In the following sequences, write down the next 3 terms and the *n*th term:

a) 7, 10, 13, 16,...

b) 12, 17, 22, 27,...

c) 6, 16, 26, 36,...

d) 54, 61, 68, 75,...

Q5 10, 20, 15, 17½, 16¼...

a) Write down the next 4 terms.

b) Explain how you would work out the 10th term.

Z Coordinates and Line Segments

Q1   Find the midpoint of the line AB, where A and B have coordinates:

a) A(2,3) B(4,5)

b) A(1,8) B(10,2)

c) A(0,11) B(11,11)

d) A(3,15) B(14,3)

e) A(6,7) B(0,0)

f) A(16,16) B(3,3)

g) A(8,33) B(32,50)

h) A(17,28) B(44,13)

ahh... nice'n'easy...

Your answers should be coordinates too.

Q2   Anna is designing the plan of a kitchen using some computer aided design software. The coordinates of the room on screen are (0, 10), (220, 10), (0, 260), (220, 260). She needs to enter the coordinates of the ceiling light, which will be exactly in the centre of the room. What will the coordinates of the light be?

Q3   Find the midpoints of each of these lines:

a) Line PQ, where P has coordinates (–1,5) and Q has coordinates (5,6).

b) Line AB, where A has coordinates (–3,3) and B has coordinates (4,0).

c) Line RS, where R has coordinates (4,–5) and S has coordinates (0,0).

d) Line PQ, where P has coordinates (–1,–3) and Q has coordinates (3,1).

e) Line GH, where G has coordinates (10,13) and H has coordinates (–6,–7).

f) Line CD, where C has coordinates (–4,6) and D has coordinates (12,–7).

g) Line MN, where M has coordinates (–5,–8) and N has coordinates (–21,–17).

h) Line AB, where A has coordinates (–1,0) and B has coordinates (–9,–14).

Q4   The diagram shows a cuboid. Vertices A and H have coordinates (1, 2, 8) and (4, 5, 3) respectively. Write down the coordinates of all the other vertices.

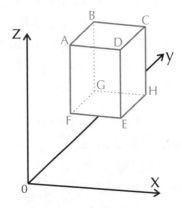

B (.... , ... , ...)

C (.... , ... , ...)

D (.... , ... , ...)

E (.... , ... , ...)

F (.... , ... , ...)

G (.... , ... , ...)

y = mx + c

Writing the equation of a line in the form y = mx + c gives you a nifty way of finding the gradient and y-intercept. Remember that — it'll save you loads of time. Anything for an easy life...

Q1 For each of the following lines, give the gradient and the coordinates of the point where the line cuts the *y*-axis.

I know these are a bit algebra-ish, but don't worry, they won't bite.

a) $y = 4x + 3$

b) $y = 3x - 2$

c) $y = -3x + 3$

d) $y = -6x - 4$

e) $y = x$

f) $y = -\frac{1}{2}x + 3$

g) $3y = 4x + 6$

h) $2y = -5x - 4$

i) $3y = 7x + 5$

j) $x + y = 0$

k) $x - y = 0$

l) $y - 7 = 3x$

m) $y - 5x = 3$

n) $y + 2x + 3 = 0$

Q2 Find the equations of the following lines:

a) A

b) B

c) C

d) D

e) E

f) F

Yeah, OK, this sounds a bit scary, but just work out the gradient (m) and look at the y-intercept (c) and pop them back into "y = mx + c"... easy lemons.

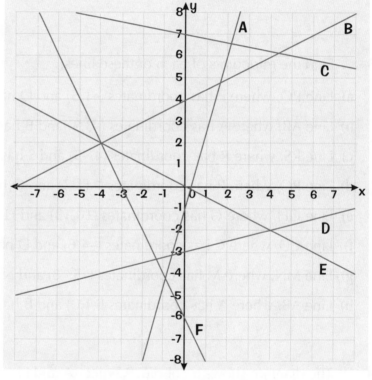

Q3 Find the equation of the straight line which passes through:

a) (3, 7) and has a gradient of 1

b) (–3, 3) and has a gradient of 2

c) (–1, 7) and has a gradient of –3

d) (4, –11) and has a gradient of –2.

Q4 Write down the equation of the line which passes through the points:

a) (2, 2) and (5, 5)

b) (–2, –3) and (5, 11)

c) (1, 0) and (5, –12)

d) (–5, 6) and (–1, –2)

Here's a bit more practice with those gradients. Thought you'd like that.

More Graphs

You need to remember what the different bits of a travel graph mean — what it looks like when <u>stopped</u>, <u>changing speed</u> and <u>coming back</u> to the starting point.

Q1 Dave drives a bus from Kendal to Ingleton and back again. The bus company graphed the journey to help them organise their bus schedules.
a) How long did it take to get to Ingleton?
b) How much time was spent driving to and from Ingleton excluding stops?
c) What was the average speed for the journey from Kendal to Ingleton?
d) What was Dave's fastest speed?
e) The transport manager wants Dave to reduce the duration of the stops on the Kendal to Ingleton route so that he can make another journey from Kendal to Windermere starting at 1630. Would this be possible?

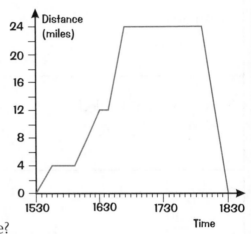

Q2 A train operator plans to purchase a new engine. They've graphed the journeys made by five engines over a 100 km stretch of track to help them decide which one is best.
a) Calculate the speed of each train and state which one was the fastest.
b) How could you tell by looking at the diagram which was the fastest and which was the slowest?

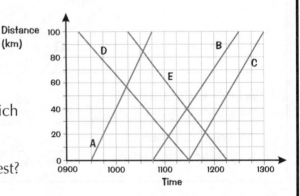

Q3 On sports day the first three in the 1000 m race ran as shown in the graph below.
a) Which runner, A, B or C, won the race?
b) How long did the winner take?
c) Which runner kept up a steady speed?
d) What was that speed
  i) in m/min?   **ii)** km/h?
e) Which runner achieved the fastest speed and what was that speed?

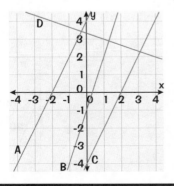

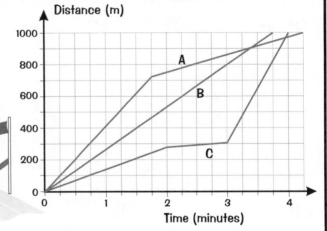

Q4 Look at the graph on the left.
a) Which two lines have the same gradient?
b) Line D is perpendicular to line B. The equation of line B is $y = 3x - 1$. Find the gradient of line D.

Geometry

 Here are some angle rules then — just the 7 for now. You can't get away without knowing these, I'm afraid, so get learning.

1) Angles in a triangle <u>add up to 180°</u>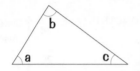

2) Angles in a 4-sided shape <u>add up to 360°</u>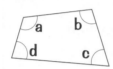

3) Angles round a point <u>add up to 360°</u>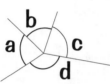

4) When a line crosses <u>TWO PARALLEL LINES</u>, the two bunches of angles are the same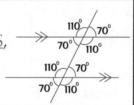

5) Angles on a straight line <u>add up to 180°</u>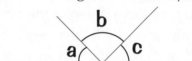

6) <u>ISOSCELES TRIANGLES</u> have two sides the same and two angles the same

7) <u>EXTERIOR</u> angle of a triangle = sum of opposite <u>INTERIOR</u> angles.

d = a + b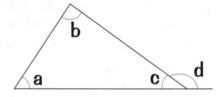

For the following diagrams, find the <u>lettered</u> angles.   LM is a straight line.

Q1 a)    **b)**   **c)**   **d)**

Q2 a)    **b)** 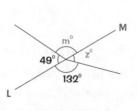   **c)** 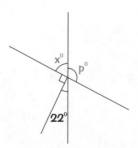   **d)**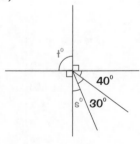

Geometry

This page is a bit dull — just lots of boring angles... still, that's geometry for you. Oh and by the way, you've got to work the angles out — don't try and sneakily measure them, they're probably drawn wrong anyway...

For the following diagrams, find the <u>lettered</u> angles.   LM is a straight line.

Q3 a)

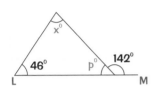

b)

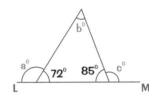

c)

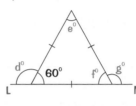

d)

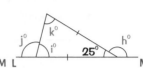

Q4 a)

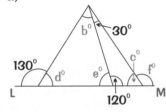

b)

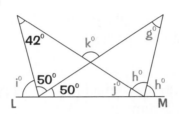

c)

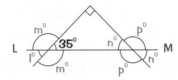

Keep an eye out for parallel lines and vertically opposite angles — they'll help no end... as long as you can remember the rules, of course.

Q5 a)

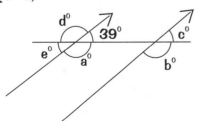

b)

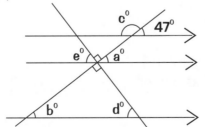

c)

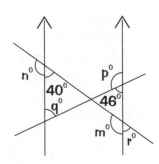

Q6 a)

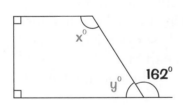

b)

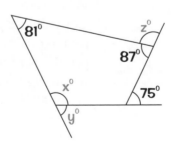

c)

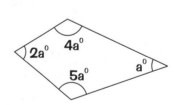

Polygons

The one thing they're <u>guaranteed</u> to ask you about is <u>Interior and Exterior Angles</u> — you'd better get learning those formulas...

> A <u>POLYGON</u> is a many-sided shape. A <u>REGULAR</u> polygon is one where <u>ALL THE SIDES AND ANGLES ARE THE SAME</u>.

> You need to know these two formulas:
> 1) EXTERIOR ANGLE = 360° ÷ No. of Sides
> 2) INTERIOR ANGLE = 180° − EXTERIOR ANGLE

Q1 What sort of triangles occur in every <u>regular polygon</u> when each vertex is joined to the centre by a straight line?

Q2 Using a compass, construct an <u>equilateral</u> triangle with sides of 3 cm. What is the interior angle at each vertex?

Q3 Sketch a regular hexagon and draw in all its lines of symmetry. State the order of <u>rotational</u> symmetry.

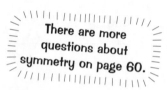

There are more questions about symmetry on page 60.

Q4 In each of the pentagons below, all the sides are of equal length, two of the angles are 90° and the other interior angles are m, m, and r degrees.

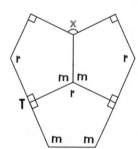

a) Explain in <u>two</u> different ways how you know that 2m + r = 360°.
b) What is the size of the exterior angle x?
c) Copy the diagram and add two more pentagons (by tracing through) so that the point T is completely surrounded and the whole figure forms part of a tessellation. Label all the angles of the new pentagons.

Q5 A square and a regular hexagon are placed adjacent to each other.
a) What is the size of ∠PQW?
b) What is the size of ∠PRW?
c) How many sides has the regular polygon that has ∠PQW as one of its angles?

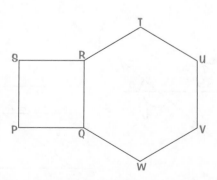

Polygons

Q6   An <u>irregular pentagon</u> has interior angles of 100°, 104°, 120°.
If the other two angles are equal, what is their size?

Q7 a) The <u>sum</u> of the <u>interior</u> angles of a <u>regular</u> 24-sided polygon is 3960°.
Use this to calculate the size of one <u>interior</u> angle.
  b) From your answer to part **a)** calculate one <u>exterior</u> angle and show that the <u>sum</u> of the
exterior angles equals 360°.

Q8   ABCDE is a regular pentagon. It is drawn in a circle centre O.
SAT is a tangent drawn to the circle at A.

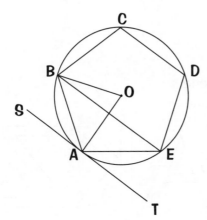

a) Calculate the size of angle BOA.
b) Find the size of angle OBA.
c) Write down the size of angle:
  i) SAO
  ii) BAS.

Q9   The sum of the interior angles of a regular polygon is 2520°.
How many sides does this regular polygon have?

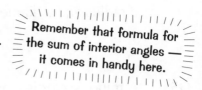

Remember that formula for the sum of interior angles — it comes in handy here.

Q10   ABCDEFGH is a regular octagon.
  a) Copy the figure and mark on the axis of
symmetry which maps H to A.
  b) Calculate the size of angle EFC.

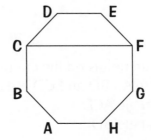

Symmetry and Circles

Q1   Draw <u>all</u> the lines of symmetry for each of the following shapes.
(Some shapes may have no lines of symmetry)

a) 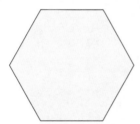   **b)**   **c)**   **d)** 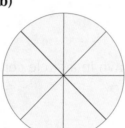   **e)**    **f)**

Q2   What is the <u>order of rotational symmetry</u> for each of the following shapes?

a)   **b)**    **c)** 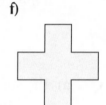   **d)**

Q3   Mark in the <u>lines of symmetry</u> of the following letters.
State the <u>order</u> of rotational symmetry for each one.

Q4   Draw a circle with radius 3 cm.
On your circle label the circumference,
a radius and a diameter.

Q5   A <u>minor sector</u> is labelled A on the diagram.
Name the features labelled B, C and D.

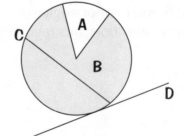

Q6   B and C are points on the circumference of a circle
with centre A. BD and CD are tangents of the circle.
a) Find the angle ACD.
b) Find the angle ADB.

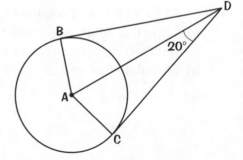

Areas and Nets

Q1 Calculate the area and perimeter of the rectangle.

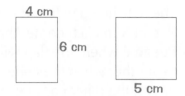

Q2 Calculate the area and perimeter of the square.

Q3 A rectangular dining room, with a width equal to half its length, needs carpet tiling.
   a) Calculate the area of the floor, if its width is 12 m.
   b) If carpet tiles are 50 cm by 50 cm squares, calculate how many tiles will be required.
   c) If carpet tiles cost £4.99 per m², calculate the <u>cost</u> of tiling the dining room.

Q4 An attachment on a child's toy is made from plastic in the shape of an octagon with a square cut out. By counting squares or otherwise, find the area of plastic needed to make 4 of these attachments.

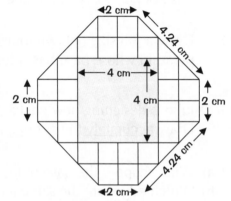

Q5 Josh is making a cube bean bag out of material for his textiles coursework. If each side of the cube is to have edges of length 60 cm, how many <u>square metres</u> of material will Josh need?

Q6 A lawn is to be made 48 m². If its width is 5 m, how long is it? How many rolls of turf 50 cm wide and 11 m long should be ordered to grass this area?

Q7 This parallelogram has an area of 4773 mm². How long is its <u>base</u>?

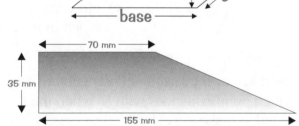

Q8 A metal blade for a craft knife is the shape of a <u>trapezium</u>. Calculate the area of the metal.

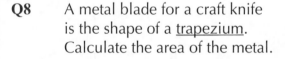

If you can't remember the formula for the area of a trapezium, you can always split the shape into a rectangle and a triangle.

Q9 A modern glass sculpture is to be erected. It is made from glass in the shape of two mountain peaks. Calculate each <u>separate</u> area and hence find the <u>total</u> area of glass required.

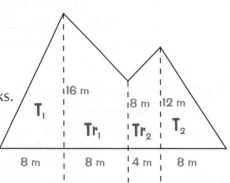

Areas and Nets

Q10 The net shown will fold to make a cube. Only one flap is shown. <u>Copy</u> the diagram.
  a) Put an X in each corner that touches Y when the cube is made up.
  b) Put an F where the flap will join one face
    to another when the cube is made up.
  c) Put on the other flaps necessary to
    glue the cube together.

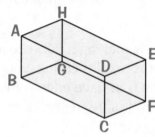

Q11 Draw an <u>accurate</u> net that would fold to make
  the 3-D cuboid shown (diagram is not full size).
  It is not necessary to include flaps.

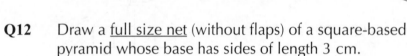

Q12 Draw a <u>full size net</u> (without flaps) of a square-based
  pyramid whose base has sides of length 3 cm.

Q13 Julie is designing new packaging boxes for her home-made jewellery.
  Draw <u>accurately</u> the net of a regular tetrahedron, with sufficient flaps to glue it together.

Q14 a) What shape is the <u>base</u> of the cuboid shown opposite?
  b) Which edges are the same length as DE?
  c) Which lengths equal CE?
  d) Which lengths equal the diagonal DG?
  e) How many vertices does the cuboid have?

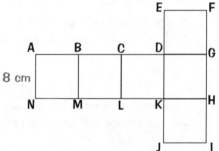

Q15

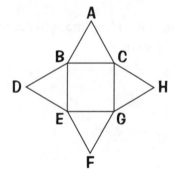

The diagram shows the net of a solid in which ABC
is an equilateral triangle and BCGE is a square.
  a) Which points will coincide with A when the net is
    folded up to make the solid?
  b) Describe the symmetry of the net.
  c) How many faces, edges and vertices does it have
    when in solid form?

Q16 The diagram shows the net of a cube of edge 8 cm.
  a) Which point coincides with M when the net is
    folded to make the cube?
  b) Find the area of the face DGHK.
  c) What is the total surface area of the cube?
  d) Use isometric paper to draw a 3-D scale
    drawing of the completed cube.

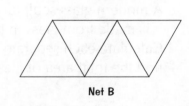

Q17 Which of these two nets will
  form a pyramid on a triangular
  base with all four faces
  equilateral triangles?

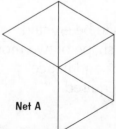
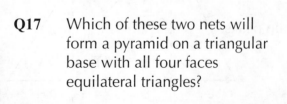

Net A   **Net B**

Volume and Projections

Q1 The diagram shows an isometric projection of a triangular prism.

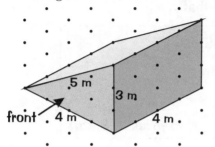

Draw:
a) the front elevation
b) the side elevation
c) the plan.

Q2 Steve has bought a pair of speaker stands. The base of each stand is a hollow prism with the dimensions shown.

Steve is filling the bases of the stands with sand to improve stability. Find the volume of sand Steve needs to use to fill both bases.

Give your answer in litres to 2 d.p.

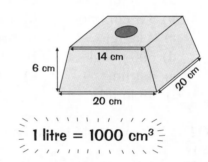

1 litre = 1000 cm³

Q3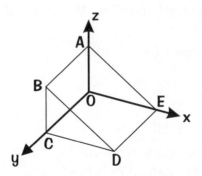

Jill buys a bookshelf with the dimensions shown in the diagram.
a) Find the cross-sectional area.
b) Find the volume of the bookshelf in m³.

Q4

The diagram shows a triangular prism.
The coordinates of A are (0, 0, 5).
The coordinates of E are (4, 0, 0).
The coordinates of C are (0, 8, 0).
a) Write down the coordinates of:
  i) B
  ii) D.
b) Calculate the volume of the prism.

Q5 Bill has a greenhouse with dimensions as shown.
The roof is made up of eight panels of equal size.

A storm breaks all of the glass in the shaded area on the diagram.

Calculate the area of glass which Bill must buy to repair his greenhouse.

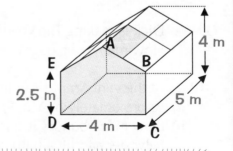

Look for a right-angled triangle to calculate AB.

Metric and Imperial Units

You've got to know all the metric and imperial conversion factors — there's no way out of it, you'll just have to sit down and learn them, sorry and all that...

> ### APPROXIMATE CONVERSIONS
>
> 1 kg ≈ 2.2 lbs   1 gallon ≈ 4.5 litres
>
> 1 litre ≈ 1¾ pints   1 foot ≈ 30 cm
>
> 1 inch ≈ 2.5 cm   1 mile ≈ 1.6 km (or 5 miles ≈ 8 km)

Q1 Express the given quantity in the unit(s) in brackets:

a) 2 m [cm]	**g)** 87 in [ft and in]	**m)** 6 ft [in]	**s)** 8 cm 6 mm [mm]
b) 3.3 cm [mm]	**h)** 43 oz [lb and oz]	**n)** 5 lb [oz]	**t)** 3 ft 6 in [in]
c) 4 kg [g]	**i)** 650 m [km]	**o)** 301 ft [yd and ft]	**u)** 4 lb 7 oz [oz]
d) 600 g [kg]	**j)** 9 kg [g]	**p)** 6 m [mm]	**v)** 550 kg [tonnes]
e) 4 ft [in]	**k)** 7 g [kg]	**q)** 2 tonnes [kg]	**w)** 3 m 54 cm [cm]
f) 36 in [ft]	**l)** 950 g [kg]	**r)** 3000 g [kg]	**x)** 0.7 cm [mm]

Q2 Convert 147 kg into pounds.

Q3 A horse's drinking trough holds 14 gallons of water.
Approximately how many litres is this?

Q4 Deborah is filling in a health questionnaire. She needs to write down her weight in kilograms. She weighs 9 stone 4 pounds. There are 14 pounds in a stone and 1 kilogram is equal to 0.157 stone. How much does Deborah weigh in kilograms?

Q5 A pile of bricks weighs 7 metric tonnes. Approximately how many imperial tons is this?

Q6 Barbara cycled 51 km in one day while Barry cycled 30 miles. Who cycled further?

Q7 A seamstress needs to cut an 11 inch strip of finest Chinese silk.
a) Approximately how many cm is this?
b) Approximately how many mm is this?

Q8 The priceless Greek statue in my garden is 21 feet tall.

a) How many inches is this?   **d)** How many cm is this?
b) How many yards is this?   **e)** How many mm is this?
c) How many metres is this?   **f)** How many km is this?

Q9 Dick is making The World's Wobbliest Jelly. The recipe requires 5 lb of sugar. How many 1 kg bags of sugar does Dick need to buy so that he can make the jelly?

Q10 At the gym Arnold can lift a barbell weighing 60 kg.
a) Approximately how many lbs is this?
b) How many ounces is this?
Sylvester can lift a barbell weighing 0.059 tonnes.
c) Who can lift the most?

Speed, Distance and Time

This is an easy enough formula — and of course you can put it in that good old formula triangle as well.

$$\text{Average speed} = \frac{\text{Total distance}}{\text{Total time}}$$

Q1 A train travels 240 km in 4 hours. What is its <u>average speed</u>?

Q2 A car travels for 3 hours at an average speed of 55 mph. How far has it travelled?

Q3 A boy rides a bike at an average speed of 15 km/h. How long will it take him to ride 40 km?

Q4 <u>Complete</u> this table.

Distance Travelled	Time taken	Average Speed
210 km	3 hrs	
135 miles		30 mph
	2 hrs 30 mins	42 km/h
9 miles	45 mins	
640 km		800 km/h
	1 hr 10 mins	60 mph

Q5 An athlete can run 100 m in 11 seconds.
Calculate the athlete's speed in:
a) m/s
b) km/h

Q6 A plane flies over city A at 09.55 and over city B at 10.02. What is its <u>average</u> speed if these cities are 63 miles apart?

Q7 The distance from Kendal (Oxenholme) to London (Euston) is 260 miles. The train travels at an average speed of 71 mph. Pete needs to be in London by 10.30. If he catches the 07.05 from Kendal, will he be in London on time? <u>Show all your working</u>.

Q8 In a speed trial a sand yacht travelled a measured mile in 36.4 seconds.
a) Calculate this speed in mph.
   On the return mile he took 36.16 seconds.
b) Find his <u>total time</u> for the two runs.
c) Calculate the average speed of the two runs in mph.

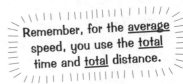

Remember, for the <u>average</u> speed, you use the <u>total</u> time and <u>total</u> distance.

Q9 A motorist drives from Manchester to London. 180 miles is on motorway where he averages 65 mph. 55 miles is on city roads where he averages 28 mph, 15 miles is on country roads where he averages 25 mph.
a) Calculate the total time taken for the journey.
b) How far did he travel altogether?
c) Calculate the average speed for the journey.

UNIT 2 — NUMBER, ALGEBRA AND GEOMETRY 1

Calculating with Standard Index Form

This stuff gets a lot easier if you know how to handle your calculator — read and learn.

Standard Index Form with a Calculator

Use the **EXP** button (or **EE** button) to enter numbers in standard index form.

Eg $1.7 \times 10^9 + 2.6 \times 10^{10}$ **1** **.** **7** **EXP** **9** **+** **2** **.** **6** **EXP** **10** **=**

The answer is 2.77^{10} which is read as 2.77×10^{10}

Q1   If $x = 4 \times 10^5$ and $y = 6 \times 10^4$ work out the value of
    a) xy **b)** $4x$ **c)** $3y$.

Q2   Which is <u>greater</u>, 4.62×10^{12} or 1.04×10^{13}, and <u>by how much</u>?

Q3   Which is <u>smaller</u> 3.2×10^{-8} or 1.3×10^{-9} and <u>by how much</u>?

Q4   The following numbers are <u>not</u> written in standard index form. Rewrite them correctly using standard index form.

    a) 42×10^6 **d)** 11.2×10^{-5} **g)** 17×10^{17}
    b) 38×10^{-5} **e)** 843×10^3 **h)** 28.3×10^{-5}
    c) 10×10^6 **f)** 42.32×10^{-4} **i)** 10×10^{-3}

> Don't forget — when you're using a calculator, you've got to write the answer as 3.46×10^{27}, <u>not</u> as 3.46^{27}. If you do it the wrong way, it means something <u>completely</u> different.

Q5   What is <u>7 million</u> in standard index form?

Q6   The radius of the Earth is 6.38×10^3 km. What is the radius of the Earth measured in <u>cm</u>? Leave your answer in standard form.

Q7   One atomic mass unit is equivalent to 1.661×10^{-27} kg. What are <u>two</u> atomic mass units equivalent to (in standard index form)?

Q8   The length of a light year, the distance light can travel in one year, is 9.461×10^{15} m. How far can light travel in
    a) 2 years?
    b) 6 months?
    Write your answers in <u>standard form</u>.

Q9 **a)** The surface area of the Earth is approximately 5.1×10^8 km². Write this <u>without</u> using standard form.
    b) The area of the Earth covered by sea is 362 000 000 km². Write this in standard form.
    c) What is the approximate area of the Earth covered by land? Write your answer <u>without</u> using standard form.

Proportion and Variation

Q1   If 17 textbooks cost £150.45, how much will 28 cost?

Q2   If it takes 4 people 28 hours to complete a task, how long would it take just one person?

Q3   A person earns £6.20 an hour. How much do they earn for 15½ hours work?

Q4   On a map, 2 cm represents 3 km.
    a) If two towns are 14 km apart, what is the distance between them on the map?
    b) If two road junctions are 20.3 cm apart on the map, what is their real distance apart?

Q5 y is directly proportional to x. If $y = 5$ when x is 25, find y when x is 100.

Q6 y is directly proportional to x. If y is 1.2 when x is 2.5, find the value of y when $x = 3.75$.

Q7   If $y \propto x$ and $y = 132$ when $x = 10$, find the value of y when $x = 14$.

Q8   If $y \propto x$ and $y = 117$ when $x = 45$, find the value of x when $y = 195$.

Q9   Complete the following tables of values where y is always directly proportional to x.

    a)

X	2	4	6
y	5	10	

    b)

X	3	6	9
y		9	

    c)

X	27		
y	5	10	15

Q10   If $y = 3$ when $x = 8$ and y is inversely proportional to x, find the value of y when $x = 12$.

Q11   If $y \propto \dfrac{1}{x}$ and $x = 4$ when $y = 5$, find the value of x when $y = 10$.

Q12   If y and x vary inversely, and $y = 12$ when $x = 3$ find:
    a) the value of x when $y = 9$
    b) the value of y when $x = 6$.

Q13   On a daytrip, a man takes 2 hours to get to the seaside from his
home, travelling at 72 km per hour. If he can do the return journey
at a speed of 80 km per hour, how long will it take him?

Q14   Given that $y \propto \dfrac{1}{x}$, complete this table of values.

X	1	2	3	4	5	6
y					9.6	

Put the numbers into the equation $y = k/x$ to find the value of k. Then you can find the rest of the ys.

Make sure you know the 4 main details about Direct and Inverse Proportion:
1) what happens when one quantity increases,
2) the graph,
3) the table of values and
4) whether it's the ratio or the product that's the same for all values.

Proportion and Variation

Q15 The area of a circle is proportional to the square of the radius. If the area is 113 cm²
when the radius is 6 cm, find:
a) the area of a circle with radius 5 cm
b) the radius of a circle with area 29 cm².
Give your answers to 1 d.p.

Q16 If $y \propto x^2$ and $y = 4$ when $x = 4$, find the value of y when $x = 12$.

Q17 $y = kx^3$ and $y = 200$ when $x = 5$.
a) Find the value of k.
b) Find the value of y when $x = 8$.
c) Find the value of x when $y = 2433.4$.

Q18 Given that y varies inversely as the square of x, complete the following table of values,
given that x is always positive.

X	1	2	5	
y			4	1

X	2			8
y	24	6	2⅔	

Q19 Two cylindrical containers are filled
to the same depth, d cm, with water.
The mass of the water in each container
is proportional to the square of the
radius of each container. The first
container has a radius of 16 cm and
the water has a mass of 16 kg. If the
second container has a radius of 8 cm,
find the mass of the water inside it.

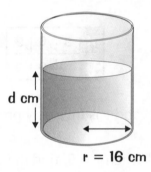

d cm   r = 16 cm   d cm   r = 8 cm

Q20 Given that r varies inversely as the square of s, and $r = 24$ when $s = 10$, find the values of:
a) r when $s = 5$
b) s when $r = 150$, given that s is positive
c) r when $s = 2$
d) s when $r = 37\frac{1}{2}$, given that s is negative

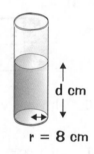

Don't forget about that little joker,
the "inverse square" variation — they'll
expect you to know that, too.

Q21 The gravitational pull of the Earth is inversely proportional to the square of the distance
from the centre of the Earth. At the Earth's surface (approx. 6371 km from the centre)
the gravitational pull is around 9.8 N kg⁻¹. When launching a satellite into space,
the gravitational pull helps determine the orbit. What would be the gravitational
pull on a satellite at a height of 100 km above the Earth's surface (to 1 d.p)?

Q22 By considering the values in the table, decide whether $y \propto x$, $y \propto \dfrac{1}{x}$ or $y \propto \dfrac{1}{x^2}$.

a) Write down the equation which shows
how y varies with x.
b) Find the value of y when $x = 6.4$
c) Find the value of x when $y = 16$.

X	1.2	2.5	3.2	4.8
y	166⅔	80	62.5	41⅔

Percentage and Proportion Change

Working out "something % of something else" is dead easy. Just remember to add it back on to the original amount if you've got a **VAT** question.

Q1  Four friends stay at the Pickled Parrot Hotel for a night and each have an evening meal. Bed and Breakfast costs £37 per person and the evening meal costs £15 per person. How much is the total cost, if VAT is added at 17½%?

Q2 Donald earns an annual wage of £23 500. He doesn't pay tax on the first £6400 that he earns. How much income tax does he pay a year if the rate of tax is:
a) 25%
b) 40%?

Q3 I wish to invest £1000 for a period of three years and have decided to place my money with the Highrise Building Society on 1 January. If I choose to use the Gold Account I will withdraw the interest at the end of each year. If I choose to use the Silver Account I will leave the interest to be added to the capital at the end of each year.

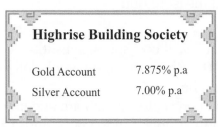

Highrise Building Society

Gold Account   7.875% p.a

Silver Account   7.00% p.a

a) Calculate the total interest I will receive if I use the Gold Account.
b) Calculate the total interest I will receive if I use the Silver Account.
   After some thought I decide to use the Gold Account and leave the interest to be added to the capital at the end of each year.
c) Calculate the total interest I will now receive from the Gold Account.

Q4 If $L = MN$, what is the percentage increase in L if M increases by 15% and N increases by 20%?

Ooh... finding the <u>original value</u>. The bit most people get wrong is deciding whether the value given represents <u>more</u> or <u>less than 100%</u> of the original — so <u>always</u> check your answer <u>makes sense</u>.

Q5 In the new year sales Robin bought a tennis racket for £68.00.
The original price had been reduced by 15%. What was the original price?

Q6 There are 360 people living in a certain village.
The population of the village has grown by 20% over the past year.
a) How many people lived in the village one year ago?
b) If the village continues to grow at the same rate, how many whole years from today will it be before the population is more than twice its current size?

Bounds and Reciprocals

To find the upper or lower bound of a calculation, you've just got to decide which version of the values involved (max or min) to use to get the biggest or smallest overall answer.

Q1 Jodie weighs herself on some scales that are accurate to the nearest 10 grams. The digital display shows her weight as 64.78 kg.
a) What is the maximum that she could weigh?
b) What is the minimum that she could weigh?

Q2 A rectangular rug is 1.8 metres long and 0.7 metres wide. Both measurements are given correct to one decimal place.
a) State the minimum possible length of the rug.
b) Calculate the maximum possible area of the rug.

Q3 It's Pancake Day and Nigel is making a large batch of pancakes to share with friends. His recipe tells him to add 2.5 litres of milk, but his measuring jug only measures up to 500 ml and is accurate to the nearest 10 ml.
a) What is the maximum volume of milk Nigel could measure out, assuming he is as accurate as he can be?
b) What is the minimum volume of milk Nigel could measure out?

Q4 Sandra has a parcel to post. To find out how much it will cost she weighs it.
a) A set of kitchen scales, that weigh to the nearest 10 g, show that the parcel weighs 90 g. Write down the largest weight that the parcel could be.
b) Next she weighs the parcel on a different set of kitchen scales, which are accurate to the nearest 5 g. The packet weighs 95 g. Write down the upper and lower bounds of the weight of the package according to these scales.
c) The post office weighs the parcel on some electronic scales to the nearest gram. It weighs 98 g. Can all the scales be right?

Q5 $R = \dfrac{S}{T}$ is a formula used by stockbrokers.
$S = 940$, correct to 2 significant figures and $T = 5.56$, correct to 3 significant figures.
a) For the value of S, write down the upper bound and the lower bound.
b) For the value of T, write down the upper bound and the lower bound.
c) Calculate the upper bound and lower bound for R.
d) Write down the value of R correct to an appropriate number of significant figures.

> **Remember** — you don't always get the maximum value by using the biggest input values.

Q6 $A = 13$, correct to 2 significant figures.
$B = 12.5$, correct to 3 significant figures.
a) For the value of A, write down the upper bound and the lower bound.
b) For the value of B, write down the upper bound and the lower bound.
c) Calculate the upper bound and lower bound for C when $C = AB$.

Bounds and Reciprocals

Q7 Ash wants to put a new carpet in his living room. He has measured the floor as being 3.4 m × 5.2 m to the nearest 10 cm. What area of carpet should Ash buy to make sure he has enough to cover the whole floor?

Q8 Vince ran a 100 m race in 10.3 seconds. If the time was measured to the nearest 0.1 seconds and the distance to the nearest metre, what is the maximum value of his average speed, in metres per second?

Q9 A lorry travelled 125 kilometres in 1 hour and 50 minutes. If the time was measured to the nearest 10 minutes and the distance to the nearest five kilometres, what was the maximum value of the average speed of the lorry, in kilometres per hour?

Q10 Jimmy, Sarah and Douglas are comparing their best times for running the 1500 m.
Jimmy's best time is 5 minutes 30 seconds measured to the nearest 10 seconds.
Sarah's best time is also 5 minutes 30 seconds, but measured to the nearest 5 seconds.
Douglas' best time is 5 minutes 26 seconds measured to the nearest second.

a) What are the upper and lower bounds for Sarah's best time?
b) Of the three, Douglas thinks that he is the quickest at running the 1500 m. Explain why this may not be the case.

Q11 Write down the reciprocals of the following values.
Leave your answers as whole numbers or fractions.

a) 7 **b)** 12 **c)** $\frac{3}{8}$ **d)** $-\frac{1}{2}$

Q12 Use your calculator to work out the reciprocals of the following values.
Write your answers as whole numbers or decimals.

a) 12 **b)** $\sqrt{2}$ **c)** π **d)** 0.008

Solving Equations

Q1 When 1 is added to a number and the answer then trebled, it gives the same result as doubling the number and then adding 4. Find the number.

Q2 Solve the following:
   a) $2x^2 = 18$ **b)** $2x^2 = 72$ **c)** $3x^2 = 27$ **d)** $4x^2 = 36$ **e)** $5x^2 = 5$

Q3 Solve the following:
   a) $3x + 1 = 2x + 6$ **c)** $5x - 1 = 3x + 19$ **e)** $x + 15 = 4x$

   b) $4x + 3 = 3x + 7$ **d)** $x + 2 = \frac{1}{2}x - 1$ **f)** $3x + 3 = 2x + 12$

Q4 Solve the following:
   a) $3x - 8 = 7$ **d)** $2x - 9 = 25$ **f)** $5x - 2 = 6x - 7$

   b) $2(x - 3) = -2$ **g)** $30 - \frac{x^2}{2} = 28$

   c) $4(2x - 1) = 60$ **e)** $\frac{24}{x} + 2 = 6$

Q5
   A square has sides of length $(x + 1)$ cm. Find the value of x if:

      a) the perimeter of the square is 66 cm
      b) the perimeter of the square is 152.8 cm.

With these wordy ones, you just have to write your own equation from the information you're given.

Q6 Mr Smith sent his car to the local garage. He spent £x on new parts, four times this amount on labour and finally £29 for an MOT test. If the total bill was for £106.50, find the value of x.

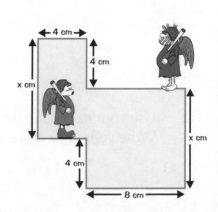

Q7 Solve:
   a) $2(x - 3) - (x - 2) = 5$ **g)** $\frac{x}{3} + 7 = 12$ **j)** $41 - \frac{x}{11} = 35$

   b) $5(x + 2) - 3(x - 5) = 29$

   c) $2(x + 2) + 3(x + 4) = 31$ **h)** $\frac{x}{10} + 18 = 29$ **k)** $\frac{x}{100} - 3 = 4$

   d) $10(x + 3) - 4(x - 2) = 7(x + 5)$

   e) $5(4x + 3) = 4(7x - 5) + 3(9 - 2x)$ **i)** $17 - \frac{x^2}{3} = 5$ **l)** $\frac{120}{x} = 16$

   f) $3(7 + 2x) + 2(1 - x) = 19$

Q8 Joan, Kate and Linda win £2400 in a lottery between them. Joan gets a share of £x, whilst Kate gets twice as much as Joan. Linda's share is £232 less than Joan's amount.
   a) Write down an expression for the amounts Joan, Kate and Linda win.
   b) Write down an equation in terms of x, and solve it.
   c) Write down the amounts Kate and Linda receive.

Q9 All the angles in the diagram are right angles.
   a) Write down an expression for the perimeter of the shape.
   b) Write down an expression for the area of the shape.
   c) For what value of x will the perimeter and area be numerically equal?

Big blobs and broomsticks...

Solving Equations

Q10 Solve the following:

a) $5(x - 1) + 3(x - 4) = -11$

b) $3(x + 2) + 2(x - 4) = x - 3(x + 3)$

c) $\frac{3x}{2} + 3 = x$

d) $3(4x + 2) = 2(2x - 1)$

e) $\frac{5x + 7}{9} = 3$

f) $\frac{2x + 7}{11} = 3$

It's easy — you just put the 2 bits together and there's your equation. Then all you've got to do is solve it...

Q11 For what value of x is the expression $14 - \frac{x}{2}$ equal to the value $\frac{3x - 4}{2}$?

Q12 Two men are decorating a room. One has painted 20 m² and the other only 6 m². They continue painting and manage to paint another x m² each. If the first man has painted exactly three times the area painted by the second man, find the value of x.

Q13 Carol's father was 24 years old when Carol was born. Now he is four times as old as Carol. How old is Carol?

Q14 Mr Jones is 4 years older than his wife and 31 years older than his son. Their ages add up to 82 years. If Mr Jones is x years old, find the value of x and find the ages of his wife and son.

Q15 Solve the following:

a) $\frac{y}{2} + 2 = 13$

b) $\frac{3x}{4} - 2 = 4$

c) $\frac{2z}{5} - 3 = -5$

d) $\frac{1}{5}(x - 4) = 3$

e) $\frac{2}{3}(x + 1) = 16$

f) $\frac{3}{5}(4x - 3) = 15$

g) $\frac{8}{x^2} = \frac{32}{36}$

h) $\frac{12}{5x^2} = \frac{3}{20}$

i) $\frac{14}{3x^2} = \frac{2}{21}$

Q16 A train travels at 70 mph for x hours and then at 80 mph for $3\frac{3}{4}$ hours. If the train covers 405 miles of track, find the value of x.

Q17 Solve the following:

a) $\frac{4x + 3}{2} + x = \frac{5x + 41}{4}$

Remember to do the same to the top and the bottom.

b) $\frac{5}{7}(x - 2) - \frac{3}{4}(x + 3) = -4$

Q18 A triangle has lengths as shown below. Find the length of each side, if the length of AC exceeds that of AB by ½ cm.

$(6x - 4)$ cm

$(3x + 1)$ cm

B   5x cm   C

Simultaneous Equations and Graphs

Q1   Solve the following simultaneous equations by drawing graphs. Use values $0 \leqslant x \leqslant 6$.

a) $y = x$
   $y = 9 - 2x$

b) $y = 2x + 1$
   $2y = 8 + x$

c) $y = 4 - 2x$
   $x + y = 3$

d) $y = 3 - x$
   $3x + y = 5$

e) $2x + y = 6$
   $y = 3x + 1$

f) $y = 2x$
   $y = x + 1$

g) $x + y = 5$
   $2x - 1 = y$

h) $2y = 3x$
   $y = x + 1$

i) $y = x - 3$
   $y + x = 7$

j) $y = x + 1$
   $2x + y = 10$

Q2   The diagram shows the graphs:
   $y = x^2 - x$
   $y = x + 2$
   $y = 8$
   $y = -2x + 4$

Use the graphs to find
the solutions to:

a) $x^2 - x = 0$

b) $x^2 - x = x + 2$

c) $x^2 - x = 8$

d) $x^2 - x = -2x + 4$

e) $-2x + 4 = x + 2$

f) $x^2 - x - 8 = 0$

g) $x^2 + x = 4$

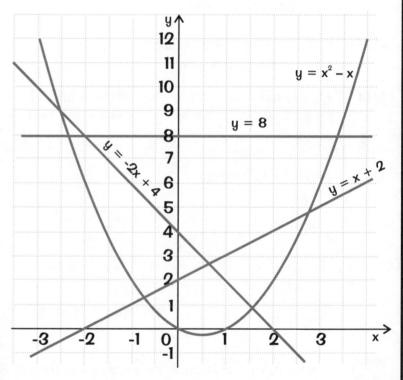

 These equations look a bit nasty, but they're just made up of the equations you've got graphs for. And you know how to do the rest of it, don't you...

Q3   Complete this table for $y = -\dfrac{1}{2}x^2 + 5$:

X	-4	-3	-2	-1	0	1	2	3	4
-½ x²									
+5									
y									

Draw the graph $y = -\dfrac{1}{2}x^2 + 5$.
Use your graph to solve the following equations (to 1 d.p.):

a) $-\dfrac{1}{2}x^2 + 5 = 0$ **b)** $-\dfrac{1}{2}x^2 + 5 = -3$ **c)** $-\dfrac{1}{2}x^2 + 5 = x$

Simultaneous Equations

To solve simultaneous equations from scratch, you've got to get rid of
either x or y first — to leave you with an equation with just one unknown in it.

Q1   Use the linear equation (the one with no x^2s in it) to find an expression for y. Then
substitute it into the quadratic equation (the one <u>with</u> x^2s in it), to solve these equations:

a) $y = x^2 + 2$
$y = x + 14$

b) $y = x^2 - 8$
$y = 3x + 10$

c) $y = 2x^2$
$y = x + 3$

d) $x + 5y = 30$
$x^2 + \frac{4}{5}x = y$

e) $y = 1 - 13x$
$y = 4x^2 + 4$

f) $y = 3(x^2 + 3)$
$14x + y = 1$

Q2   Solve the following simultaneous equations:

a) $4x + 6y = 16$
$x + 2y = 5$

b) $3x + 8y = 24$
$x + y = 3$

c) $3y - 8x = 24$
$3y + 2x = 9$

*Careful with parts
d) to f) — some of
them are quadratics...*

d) $y = x^2 - 2$
$y = 3x + 8$

e) $y = 3x^2 - 10$
$13x - y = 14$

f) $y + 2 = 2x^2$
$y + 3x = 0$

g) $3y - 10x - 17 = 0$
$\frac{1}{3}y + 2x - 5 = 0$

h) $\frac{x}{2} - 2y = 5$
$12y + x - 2 = 0$

i) $x + y = \frac{1}{2}(y - x)$
$x + y = 2$

Q3   Two farmers are buying livestock at a market. Farmer Ed buys 6 sheep and 5 pigs
for £430 and Farmer Jacob buys 4 sheep and 10 pigs for £500.

a) If sheep cost £x and pigs cost £y, write down the
two purchases as a pair of simultaneous equations.

b) Solve for x and y.

Q4   On Farmer Ed's farm, the cats have got into the chicken coop and are causing chaos.
Falmer Ed counts, in total, 11 heads and 30 legs. How many cats and how many
chickens are in the chicken coop?

Q5   Isobel is buying pick & mix sweets. She weighs out 20 jellies and 30 toffees which come
to 230 g. She takes one of each off the scales before they get bagged up, and the weight
drops to 221 g. How much does an individual toffee weigh?

Q6   Find the value of x and y for each of the following rectangles, by first writing down a pair
of simultaneous equations and then solving them.

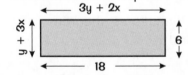

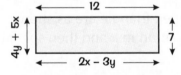

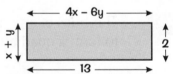

Q7   Two customers enter a shop to buy milk and cornflakes. Mrs Smith buys 5 pints of milk
and 2 boxes of cornflakes and spends £3.44. Mr Brown buys
4 pints of milk and 3 boxes of cornflakes and receives £6.03
change after paying with a £10 note. Write down a pair of
simultaneous equations and solve them to find the price in
pence of a pint of milk (m) and a box of cornflakes (c).

Q8   Solve $\frac{3(x - y)}{5} = x - 3y = x - 6.$

The Quadratic Formula

Q1 The following quadratics can be solved by factorisation, but practise using the formula to solve them.

a) $x^2 + 8x + 12 = 0$

b) $6x^2 - x - 2 = 0$

c) $x^2 - x - 6 = 0$

d) $x^2 - 3x + 2 = 0$

e) $4x^2 - 15x + 9 = 0$

f) $x^2 - 3x = 0$

g) $36x^2 - 48x + 16 = 0$

h) $3x^2 + 8x = 0$

i) $2x^2 - 7x - 4 = 0$

j) $x^2 + x - 20 = 0$

k) $4x^2 + 8x - 12 = 0$

l) $3x^2 - 11x - 20 = 0$

m) $x + 3 = 2x^2$

n) $5 - 3x - 2x^2 = 0$

o) $1 - 5x + 6x^2 = 0$

p) $3(x^2 + 2x) = 9$

q) $x^2 + 4(x - 3) = 0$

r) $x^2 = 2(4 - x)$

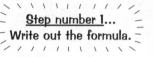

Step number 1... Write out the formula.

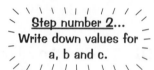

Step number 2... Write down values for a, b and c.

Step number 3... sub a, b and c into the formula. Be careful to divide the <u>whole</u> of the top line by <u>2a</u> — not just ½ of it.

Q2 Rearrange the following in the form "$ax^2 + bx + c = 0$" and then solve by the quadratic formula. Give your answers to two decimal places.

a) $x^2 = 8 - 3x$

b) $(x + 2)^2 - 3 = 0$

c) $3x(x - 1) = 5$

d) $2x(x + 4) = 1$

e) $x^2 = 4(x + 1)$

f) $(2x - 1)^2 = 5$

g) $3x^2 + 2x = 6$

h) $(x + 2)(x + 3) = 5$

i) $(x - 2)(2x - 1) = 3$

j) $2x + \frac{4}{x} = 7$

k) $(x - ½)^2 = ¼$

l) $4x(x - 2) = -3$

 Pythagoras... remember him — you know, that bloke who didn't like angles.

Q3 The sides of a right-angled triangle are as shown. Use Pythagoras' theorem to form a quadratic equation in x and then solve it to find x.

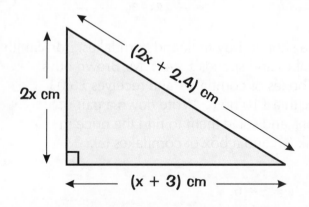

2x cm

(2x + 2.4) cm

(x + 3) cm

Completing the Square

All you're doing is writing it in the form "$(x + 4)^2 + 2$" instead of "$x^2 + 8x + 18$" — don't let the name put you off.

Q1 Complete the square for the following expressions:

a) $x^2 - 4x - 5$

b) $x^2 - 2x + 1$

c) $x^2 + x + 1$

d) $x^2 - 6x + 9$

e) $x^2 - 6x + 7$

f) $x^2 - 4x$

First look at what you need to put in the bracket to get the x^2 and x terms. Then work the number part out at the end.

g) $x^2 + 3x - 4$

h) $x^2 - x - 3$

i) $x^2 - 10x + 25$

j) $x^2 - 10x$

k) $x^2 + 8x + 17$

l) $x^2 - 12x + 35$

Q2 Solve the following quadratic equations by completing the square.
Write down your answers to no more than 2 d.p.

a) $x^2 + 3x - 1 = 0$

b) $x^2 - x - 3 = 0$

c) $x^2 + 4x - 3 = 0$

d) $x^2 + x - 1 = 0$

e) $x^2 - 3x - 5 = 0$

f) $2x^2 - 6x + 1 = 0$

g) $3x^2 - 3x - 2 = 0$

h) $3x^2 - 6x - 1 = 0$

It's quite a cunning method, really... but I admit it takes a bit of getting used to — make sure you've learnt all the steps, then it's just practice, practice...

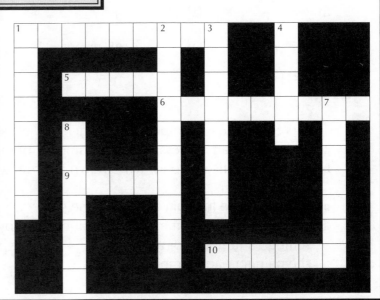

Algebra Crossword

ACROSS

1) Put brackets in (9)

5) You could do this to an equation (5)

6) There is a formula for this type of equation (9)

9) It goes with improvement (5)

10) Complete this shape (6)

DOWN

1) You should rearrange these (8)

2) $x \leqslant -6$ is an example of an _____ (10)

3) $2x + 4 = 6$ is one (8)

4) Some things grow, others _____ (5)

7) It's a type of proportion (7)

8) These are found a lot in algebra (and post boxes) (7)

Rearranging Formulas

Rearranging is getting the letter you want out of the formula and making it the subject. And it's exactly the same method as for solving equations, which can't be bad.

Q1 Rearrange the following formulas to make the letter in brackets the new subject.

a) $g = 10 - 4h$ (h)

b) $d = \frac{1}{2}(c + 4)$ (c)

c) $j = -2(3 - k)$ (k)

d) $a = \frac{2b}{3}$ (b)

e) $f = \frac{3g}{8}$ (g)

f) $y = \frac{x}{2} - 3$ (x)

g) $s = \frac{t}{6} + 10$ (t)

h) $p = 4q^2$ (q)

Q2 Jason is saving up to go travelling next year and has got a temporary job selling cars. He is paid a basic wage of £500 a month, plus a bonus of £50 for each car he sells. He has a spreadsheet to keep track of his money, which calculates his wages (£w) after working for m months and selling c cars, using the following formula:
$$w = 500m + 50c$$

a) Rearrange the formula to make c the subject.

b) Find the number of cars Jason needs to sell in 11 months to earn £12 100.

Q3 The cost of hiring a car is £28 per day plus 25p per mile.

a) Find the cost of hiring the car for a day and travelling:
  i) 40 miles
  ii) 80 miles

b) Write down a formula to give the cost of hiring a car (£c) for one day, and travelling n miles.

c) Rearrange the formula to make n the subject.

d) How many miles can you travel, during one day, if you have a budget of:
  i) £34,   ii) £50,   iii) £56.50.

Q4 Rearrange the following formulas to make the letter in brackets the new subject.

a) $y = x^2 - 2$ (x)

b) $y = \sqrt{(x + 3)}$ (x)

c) $r = \left(\frac{s}{2}\right)^2$ (s)

d) $f = \frac{10 + g}{3}$ (g)

e) $w = \frac{5 - z}{2}$ (z)

f) $v = \frac{1}{3}x^2 h$ (x)

g) $v^2 = u^2 + 2as$ (a)

h) $v^2 = u^2 + 2as$ (u)

i) $t = 2\pi\sqrt{\frac{l}{g}}$ (g)

Q5 Mrs Smith buys x jumpers for £J each and sells them in her shop for a total price of £T.

a) Write down an expression for the amount of money she paid for all the jumpers.

b) Using your answer to a), write down a formula for the profit £P Mrs Smith makes selling all the jumpers.

c) Rearrange the formula to make J the subject.

d) Given that Mrs Smith makes a profit of £156 by selling 13 jumpers for a total of £364 find the price she paid for each jumper originally.

Rearranging Formulas

Q6 A website offering digital photo printing charges 12p per print plus 60p postage.

a) Find the cost of ordering:
  i) 12 prints.
  ii) 24 prints.

b) Write down a formula for the cost C, in pence, of ordering x prints.

c) Rearrange the formula to make x the subject.

d) A regular customer is looking through old receipts to check she has been charged the right amount. How many prints should she have received in each of her last three transactions if she was charged:
  i) £4.92
  ii) £6.36
  iii) £12.12.

Q7 Rearrange the following formulas, by collecting terms in x and looking for common factors, to make x the new subject.

a) $xy = z - 2x$

b) $ax = 3x + b$

c) $4x - y = xz$

d) $xy = 3z - 5x + y$

e) $xy = xz - 2$

f) $2(x - y) = z(x + 3)$

g) $xyz = x - y - wz$

h) $3y(x + z) = y(2z - x)$

Q8 Rearrange the following to make the letter in brackets the new subject.

a) $pq = 3p + 4r - 2q$ (p)

b) $fg + 2e = 5 - 2g$ (g)

c) $a(b - 2) = c(b + 3)$ (b)

d) $pq^2 = rq^2 + 4$ (q)

e) $4(a - b) + c(a - 2) = ad$ (a)

f) $\dfrac{x^2}{3} - y = x^2$ (x)

g) $\sqrt{hk^2 - 14} = k$ (k)

h) $2\sqrt{x} + y = z\sqrt{x} + 4$ (x)

i) $\dfrac{a}{b} = \dfrac{1}{3}(b - a)$ (a)

j) $\dfrac{m + n}{m - n} = \dfrac{3}{4}$ (m)

k) $\sqrt{\dfrac{(d - e)}{e}} = 7$ (e)

l) $\dfrac{x - 2y}{xy} = 3$ (y)

These are getting quite tricky — you've got to <u>collect like</u> <u>terms</u>, before you can make anything else the subject.

Q9 Rearrange the following formulas to make y the new subject.

a) $x(y - 1) = y$

b) $x(y + 2) = y - 3$

c) $x = \dfrac{y^2 + 1}{2y^2 - 1}$

d) $x = \dfrac{2y^2 + 1}{3y^2 - 2}$

Inequalities

Yet another one of those bits of Maths that looks worse than it is — these are just like equations, really, except for the symbols.

Q1 Write down the inequality represented by each diagram below.

a)
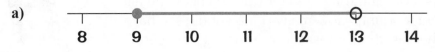

b)
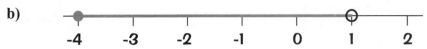

c)

d)
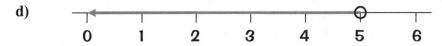

e)
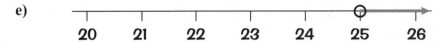

f)
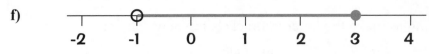

g)
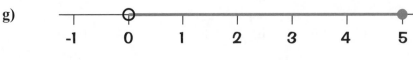

h)
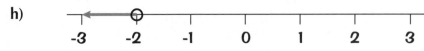

Q2 By drawing an appropriate part of the number line for each question, represent each of the following inequalities.

   a) $x > 5$ **c)** $2 > x > -5$ **e)** $3 \geq x > -2$ **g)** $-3 \leq x \leq -2$
   b) $x \leq 2$ **d)** $3 > x \geq -2$ **f)** $7 \geq x > 6$ **h)** $0 \geq x > -3$

Q3 Draw and label a number line from –5 to 5 for each of the following questions. Represent the inequalities on your number lines.

   a) $x^2 \leq 4$ **c)** $x^2 \leq 9$ **e)** $16 \geq x^2$ **g)** $9 > x^2$
   b) $x^2 < 1$ **d)** $25 \geq x^2$ **f)** $x^2 \leq 1$ **h)** $x^2 \leq 0$

Q4 Solve the following:
   a) $3x + 2 > 11$ **e)** $2x - 7 \geq 8$ **i)** $5(x + 2) \geq 25$ **m)** $8 - 3x \geq 14$
   b) $5x + 4 < 24$ **f)** $17 + 4x < 33$ **j)** $4(x - 1) > 40$ **n)** $16 - x < 11$
   c) $5x + 7 \leq 32$ **g)** $2(x + 3) < 20$ **k)** $10 - 2x > 4x - 8$ **o)** $16 - x > 1$
   d) $3x + 12 \leq 30$ **h)** $2(5x - 4) < 32$ **l)** $7 - 2x \leq 4x + 10$ **p)** $12 - 3x \leq 18$

Inequalities

Q5 Find the largest integer x, such that $2x + 5 \geq 5x - 2$.

Q6 When a number is subtracted from 11, and this new number is then divided by two, the result is always less than five. Write this information as an inequality and solve it to show the possible values of the number.

Q7 Two schools are merging and a new school is being built to accommodate all the pupils. There will be 1,130 pupils in total in the new school. No class must have more than 32 pupils. How many classrooms are needed? Show this information as an inequality.

Call the number of classrooms x.

Q8 A couple are planning their wedding. For the reception in a local hotel, they have a budget of £900. If the hotel charges £18 per head, how many guests could be invited? Show this information as an inequality.

Q9 The shaded region satisfies three inequalities. Write down these inequalities.

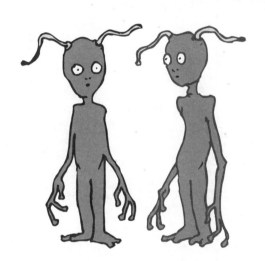

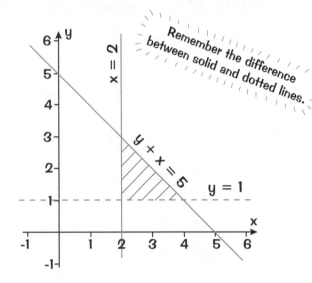

Remember the difference between solid and dotted lines.

Q10 Draw a set of axes with the x-axis from -2 to 6 and the y-axis from -1 to 7. Show on a graph the region enclosed by the following three inequalities.

$$y < 6, \qquad x + y \geq 5 \qquad \text{and} \qquad x \leq 5$$

Q11 Draw a set of axes with the x-axis from -4 to 5 and the y-axis from -3 to 6. Show on a graph the region enclosed by the following.

$$y \leq 2x + 4, \qquad y < 5 - x \qquad \text{and} \qquad y \geq \frac{x}{3} - 1$$

Q12 A company are recruiting new members of staff. All applicants must take two online tests. To get an interview, applicants must score higher than 5 on the first test, at least 7 on the second, and have a total combined score of at least 14.

  a) Write out three inequalities to represent the three criteria for getting an interview. Use x for the score on the first test and y for the score on the second test.

  b) The company want to analyse the quality of applicants by plotting their test scores on a graph, and picking out the ones who satisfy the criteria. Using suitable axes, show on a graph the region enclosed by the three inequalities where suitable candidates would be placed.

Trial and Improvement

Q1 The cubic equation $x^3 + x = 24$ has a solution between 2 and 3.
Copy the table below and use it to find this solution to 1 d.p.

Guess (x)	Value of $x^3 + x$	Too large or Too small
2	$2^3 + 2 =$	
3	$3^3 + 3 =$	

Q2 The cubic equation $x^3 + x^2 - 4x = 3$ has three solutions. The first solution lies between −3 and −2. The second lies between −1 and 0. The third solution lies between 1 and 2.
Copy the table below and use it to find all three solutions.

Guess (x)	Value of $x^3 + x^2 - 4x$	Too large or Too small
−3	$(-3)^3 + (-3)^2 - 4(-3) = -6$	
−2	$(-2)^3 + (-2)^2 - 4(-2) =$	
−1	$(-1)^3 + (-1)^2 - 4(-1) =$	
0	$(0)^3 + (0)^2 - 4(0) =$	
1	$(1)^3 + (1)^2 - 4(1) =$	
2	$(2)^3 + (2)^2 - 4(2) =$	

The first solution is

.... to 1d.p.

The second solution is

.... to 1d.p.

The third solution is

.... to 1d.p.

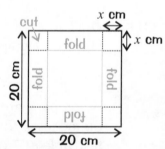

Q3 For a craft project, Steph is making some simple boxes. She cuts out squares of side length x cm from square pieces of card measuring 20 cm by 20 cm, then folds up the sides, as shown. The volume of the boxes (V) can be calculated using the cubic equation:

$$4x^3 - 80x^2 + 400x = V.$$

Use trial and improvement to find the value of x she must use to give the biggest volume of box possible, giving the answer to 1 d.p. The solution lies between 3 cm and 4 cm.

They don't always give you the starting numbers — so if they don't, make sure you pick two opposite cases (one too big, one too small), or you've blown it.

Quadratic Graphs

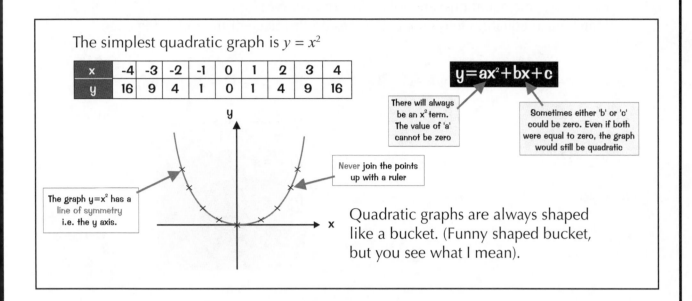

The simplest quadratic graph is $y = x^2$

x	-4	-3	-2	-1	0	1	2	3	4
y	16	9	4	1	0	1	4	9	16

$y = ax^2 + bx + c$

There will always be an x^2 term. The value of 'a' cannot be zero

Sometimes either 'b' or 'c' could be zero. Even if both were equal to zero, the graph would still be quadratic

Never join the points up with a ruler

The graph $y=x^2$ has a line of symmetry i.e. the y axis.

Quadratic graphs are always shaped like a bucket. (Funny shaped bucket, but you see what I mean).

Q1   Complete this <u>table of values</u> for the quadratic graph $y = 2x^2$.

a) Draw axes with x from -4 to 4 and y from 0 to 32.

b) Plot these 9 points and join them with a <u>smooth curve</u>.

c) Label your graph.

x	-4	-3	-2	-1	0	1	2	3	4
$y=2x^2$	32	18					8		

Remember to square first then × 2

Q2   Complete this table of values for the graph $y = x^2 + x$.

x	-4	-3	-2	-1	0	1	2	3	4
x^2	16	9					4		
$y=x^2+x$	12					2			

By putting more steps in your table of values, the arithmetic is easier

a) Draw axes with x from -4 to 4 and y from 0 to 20.

b) Plot the points and join them with a smooth curve.

c) Draw and label the <u>line of symmetry</u> for the quadratic graph $y = x^2 + x$.

If the x^2 term has a <u>minus</u> sign in front of it, the bucket will be turned <u>upside down</u>.

Q3 a) Complete this table of values for the graph $y = 3 - x^2$.

b) Draw the graph $y = 3 - x^2$ for x from -4 to 4.

c) State the <u>maximum value</u> of the graph $y = 3 - x^2$.

x	-4	-3	-2	-1	0	1	2	3	4
3	3	3	3	3	3	3	3	3	3
$-x^2$	-16						-4		
$y=3-x^2$	-13						-1		

Some Harder Graphs to Learn

Q1 Here are some equations, and there are some curves below.
Match each equation to one of the curves on this page or the following page.

a) $y = 4x - 1$

b) $y = -2x$

c) $y = -x^2$

d) $y = x^2 + 2$

e) $y = -x^2 + 3$

f) $y = -x^2 - 3$

g) $y = x^3 + 3$

h) $y = 2x^3 - 3$

i) $y = -\frac{1}{2}x^3 + 2$

j) $y = -x^3 + 3$

k) $y = x^3$

l) $y = -\frac{3}{x}$

m) $y = \frac{2}{x}$

n) $y = \frac{1}{x^2}$

o) $y = -\frac{1}{x^2}$

i)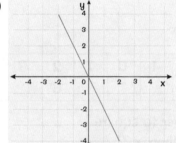

ii)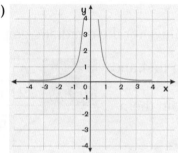

iii)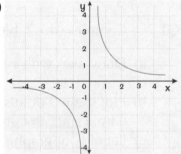

iv)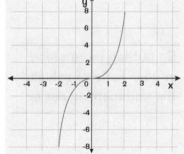

v)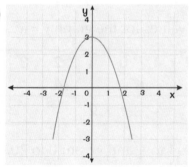

vi)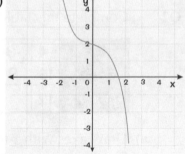

vii)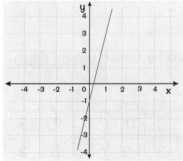

viii)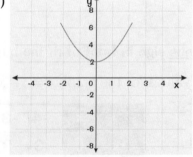

ix)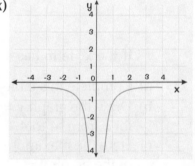

Some Harder Graphs to Learn

x)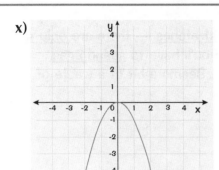

xi)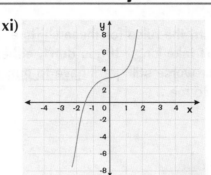

xii)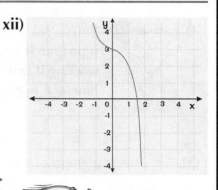

xiii)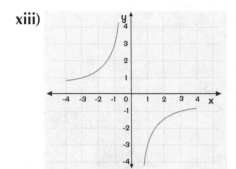

xiv)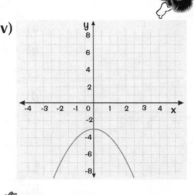

xv)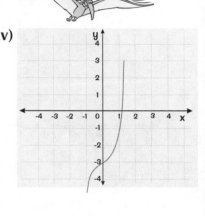

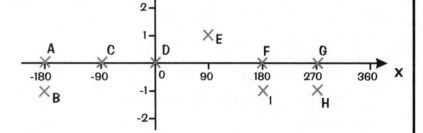

Q2 Which graph, $y = \sin(x)$ or $y = \cos(x)$, goes through the point labelled A? Which graphs go through points B to I?

Q3 Complete this table of values for $y = \cos(x) + 1$:

x	0	90	180	270	360
y	2				

Plot a graph of $y = \cos(x) + 1$ using the points in the table.

Q4 Complete this table of values for $y = x^3$:

x	-3	-2	-1	0	1	2	3
$y=x^3$							

Draw the graph of $y = x^3$.

Graphs: Shifts and Stretches

You've got to learn the rules for these <u>shifts</u> and <u>stretches</u> — there are <u>only 4</u> types, so it won't take long. If you don't, either you'll have to <u>spend ages</u> working it out, or worse still you'll <u>have to guess</u>. Seems a bit of a waste of time <u>and marks</u> to me...

Q1   This is a graph of $y = f(x)$.

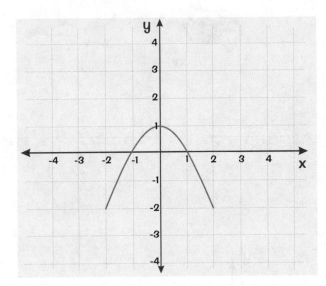

Use the graph of $y = f(x)$ to sketch:

a) $y = f(x) + 3$

b) $y = f(x) - 3$

c) $y = f(x + 3)$

d) $y = f(x - 3)$

e) $y = -f(x)$

f) $y = f(2x)$

g) $y = f(\frac{1}{2}x)$

h) $y = -f(2x)$

Q2   This is a graph of $y = f(x)$.

Use the graph of $y = f(x)$ to sketch:

a) $y = f(x) + 2$

b) $y = f(x) - 2$

c) $y = f(x + 2)$

d) $y = f(x - 2)$

e) $y = -f(x)$

f) $y = f(2x)$

g) $y = f(\frac{1}{2}x)$

h) $y = f(x + 3) - 1$

i) $y = f(x - 1) + 3$

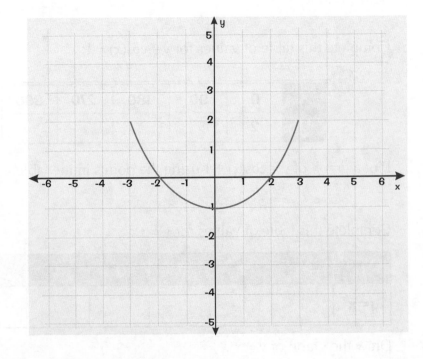

Graphs: Shifts and Stretches

Q3 A sound engineer wants to alter a recorded sound.
He brings up an image of the sound wave on a monitor, as shown below.

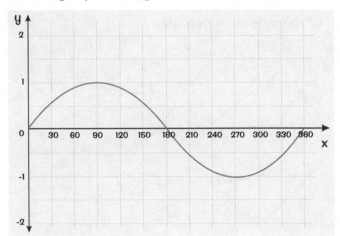

Draw what the engineer will see on the monitor if the altered sound wave has the equation:
a) $y = 2\sin(x)$
b) $y = \sin(2x)$.

Q4 This is the graph of $y = \cos(x)$:

Draw the graphs of:
a) $y = 2\cos(x)$
b) $y = \cos(2x)$.

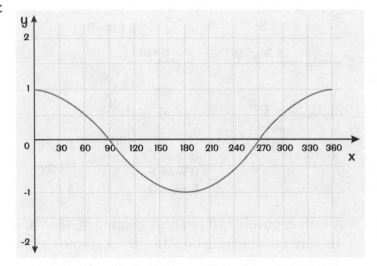

Q5 This is the graph of $y = f(x)$:
Sketch the graphs of:
a) $y = f(x) + 1$
b) $y = -f(x)$
c) $y = f(x + 1)$
d) $y = f(\frac{1}{2}x)$
e) $y = f(2x)$
f) $y = 2f(x)$
g) $y = f(x + 1) - 2$.

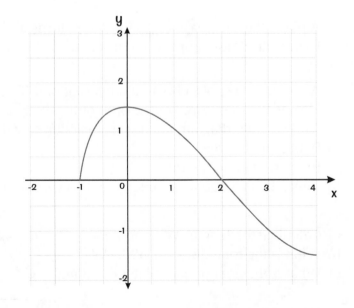

Pythagoras' Theorem and Bearings

Don't try and do it all in your head — you've got to label the sides
or you're bound to mess it up. Go on, get your pen out...

Q1 Find the unknown length in each of the following triangles.

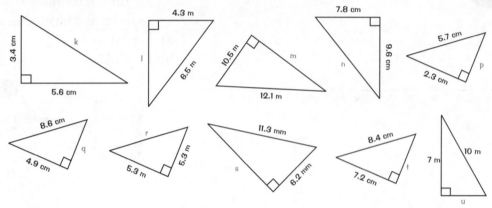

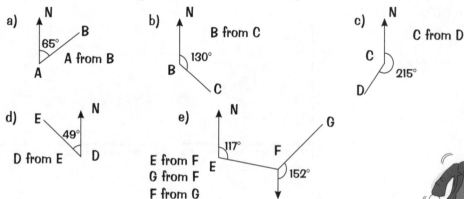

Q2 Calculate the bearings required in these diagrams.

a) N
65° B
A from B
A

b) N
B from C
130°
B
C

c) N
C from D
C
215°
D

d) E N
49°
D from E D

e) N
G
117° F
E from F E
G from F 152°
F from G

Q3 A walker travels 1200 m on a bearing of 165° and then another
1500 m on a bearing of 210°. By accurate measurement,
find how far she is now from her starting point.
What bearing must she walk on to return to base?

Q4 A plane flies due east for 153 km then turns and flies due north for 116 km.
How far is it now from where it started?

Q5 A coastguard spots a boat on a bearing of 040° and at a distance of 350 m.
He can also see a tree due east of him. The tree is due south of the boat.
 a) Draw a scale diagram and measure accurately the distances from the:
   i) boat to the tree
   ii) coastguard to the tree
 b) Check by Pythagoras to see if your answers are reasonable.

Q6 a) Calculate the lengths WY and ZY.
 b) What is the total distance WXYZW?
 c) What is the area of quadrilateral WXYZ?

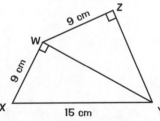

Pythagoras, Lines and Line Segments

Q1 Find the length of each of the lines on this graph.

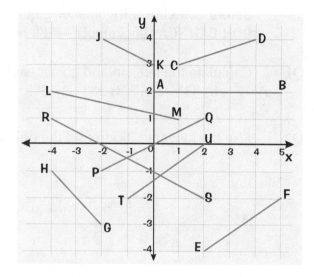

Q2 The coordinates of four points are A(2,1), B(6,4), C(7,0) and D(3,–3). Calculate the distances:
a) AB b) BC c) CD d) BD e) AC
f) What shape is ABCD?

Q3 A square tablecloth has a diagonal measurement of 130 cm. What is the length of one side?

Q4 A builder is replacing a roof beam and wants to work out how long it needs to be. It has to be the same width as the house. The measurements he already knows are shown on the diagram. How long should the beam be?

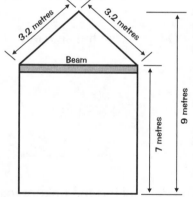

Q5 Find the length of line MN, where M and N have coordinates:
a) M(6,3) N(2,8)
b) M(1,5) N(8,12)
c) M(0,1) N(7,3)
d) M(9,5) N(4,8)
e) M(10,4) N(10,0)
f) M(12,6) N(13,0)

Q6 Find the length of line PQ, where P and Q have coordinates:
a) P(2,–3) Q(3,0)
b) P(1,–8) Q(4,3)
c) P(0,–1) Q(2,–3)
d) P(–6,–1) Q(7,–9)
e) P(12,–3) Q(–5,5)
f) P(–10,–2) Q(–2,–8)

OK, so there's a few negative numbers creeping in here, but just do them in the same way.

Q7 A flagpole 10 m high is supported by metal wires each 11 m long. How far from the foot of the pole must the wires be fastened to the ground if the other end is attached to the top of the pole?

Trigonometry — Sin, Cos, Tan

Before you start a trigonometry question, write down the ratios, using
SOH CAH TOA (Sockatoa!) — it'll help you pick your formula triangle.

Q1   Calculate the tan, sin and cos of each of these angles:
   a) 17° **b)** 83° **c)** 5° **d)** 28° **e)** 45°.

Q2   Use the tangent ratio to find the unknowns:

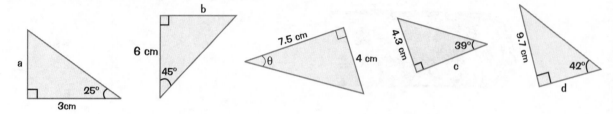

Q3   Use the cosine ratio to find the unknowns:

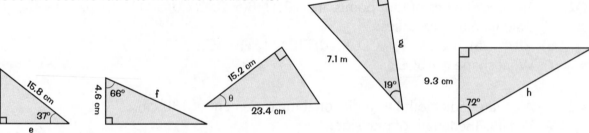

Q4   Use the sine ratio to find the unknowns:

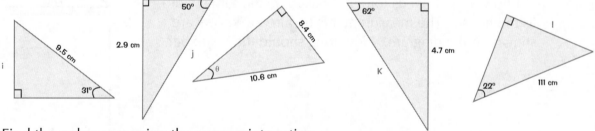

Q5   Find the unknowns using the appropriate ratios:

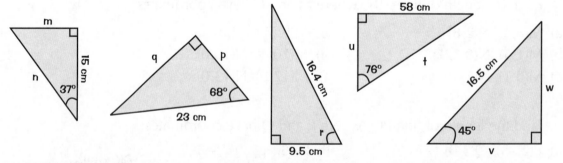

Q6   Calculate the height of the tree using the measurements in the diagram.

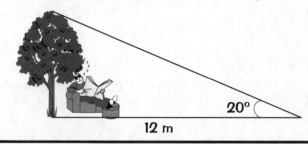

Trigonometry — Sin, Cos, Tan

Q7 A boat travels 9 km due south and then 7 km due east.
What bearing must it travel on to return to base?

Q8 This isosceles triangle has a base of 28 cm
and a top angle of 54°. Calculate:

a) the length of sides AC and BC
b) the perpendicular height to C
c) the area of the triangle.

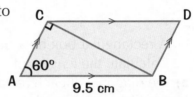

Make sure you've got the hang of the _inverse_ SIN, COS and TAN functions on your calc... and check it's in _DEG mode_ or you'll get nowhere fast.

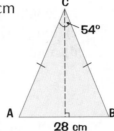

Q9 An isosceles triangle has two equal sides of 7 cm and an angle between them of 65°.
Calculate the area of the triangle.

Q10 In this parallelogram the diagonal CB is at right angles to
AC. AB is 9.5 cm and ∠CAB is 60°.
Calculate:
a) CB b) BD c) the area of the parallelogram.

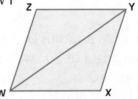

Q11 This rhombus WXYZ has base 15 cm and diagonal WY
of 28 cm. Calculate the:
a) length of diagonal XZ
b) area of the rhombus
c) angle WY makes with WX.

Q12 Two mountains are 1020 m and 1235 m high. Standing on the summit of the lower one
I look up through an angle of elevation of 16° to see the summit of the higher one.
Calculate the horizontal distance between the two mountains.

Q13 A girl is flying a kite. She holds the string, which is 45 m long, at a height of 1.3 m
above the ground. The string of the kite makes an angle of 33° with the horizontal.
What is the vertical height of the kite from the ground?

Q14 I am standing on top of an 80 m high tower. I look due north and see two cars
with angles of depression of 38° and 49°. Calculate:
a) how far each car is from the base of the tower
b) how far apart the cars are.

Q15 A ship sails on a bearing of 300° for 100 km. The captain can then see a lighthouse
due south of him that he knows is due west of his starting point.
Calculate how far west the lighthouse is from the ship's starting point.

3D Pythagoras and Trigonometry

Q1 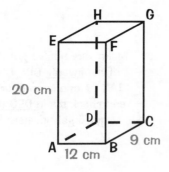 This rectangular box is 20 cm by 12 cm by 9 cm. Calculate:
- **a)** angle ABE
- **b)** length AF
- **c)** length DF
- **d)** angle EBH.

Q2 This pyramid is on a square base of side 56 cm. Its vertical height is 32 cm. Calculate the length of:
- **a)** the line from E to the mid-point of BC
- **b)** the sloping edge BE.

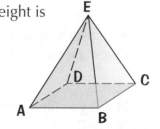

Q3 A rectangular box measures 20 cm by 30 cm by 8 cm. Calculate the lengths of:
- **a)** the diagonal of each rectangular face
- **b)** the diagonal through the centre of the box.

Q4 This glass has a radius of 2.8 cm. The straw in the glass makes an angle of 70° with the base and protrudes 4 cm above the rim.
- **a)** How tall is the glass?
- **b)** How long is the straw?

Q5 A shop sells the three different gift boxes shown on the right. Katie wants to buy the cheapest box that will fit a pen that is 10 cm long. Which box should she buy?

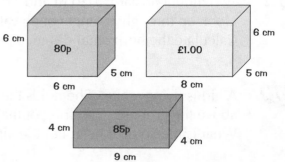

Q6 This cone has a perpendicular height of 9 cm. The centre of the base is O. The slant line from X makes an angle of 23° with the central axis. Calculate:
- **a)** the radius of the base
- **b)** the area of the base
- **c)** the volume of the cone.

The Sine and Cosine Rules

Make sure you know the Sine Rule and <u>both forms</u> of the Cosine Rule.
The one to use depends on which angles and sides you're given.

Q1 Calculate the lengths required to 3 s.f.

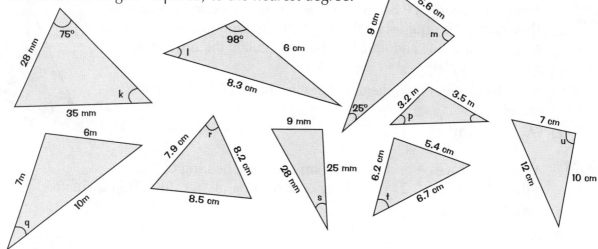

Q2 Calculate the angles required, to the nearest degree.

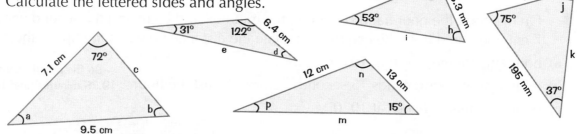

Q3 Calculate the lettered sides and angles.

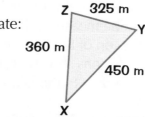

Q4 This field has measurements as shown. Calculate:
a) ∠ZXY
b) ∠XYZ
c) ∠YZX.

Q5 Peter is standing on a bridge over a river. He can see a tree on each bank, one 33 m and the other 35 m away from him. If he looks through an angle of 20° going from one tree to the other, how far apart are the two trees?

The Sine and Cosine Rules

Q6 A coastguard sees a boat on a bearing of 038° from him and 25 km away. He also sees a ship 42 km away and on a bearing of 080°. Calculate:

a) the distance of the boat from the ship

b) the bearing of the boat from the ship.

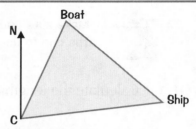

Q7 Air traffic control are testing the reliability of their computer software by monitoring two aeroplanes and checking the computer's calculations with their own. If the horizontal distance between the planes drops to 3 miles or less, an alarm should be triggered on the computer. One of the test planes is at a distance of 5 miles from the tower, and on a bearing of 020° from the tower. The second is at a distance of 4.6 miles on a bearing of 034° and the alarm is ringing. Calculate the horizontal distance between the planes and comment on the reliability of the software.

Q8 A parallelogram has sides of length 8 cm and 4.5 cm. One angle of the parallelogram is 124°. Calculate the lengths of the two diagonals.

Q9 A vertical flagpole FP has two stay wires to the ground at A and B. They cannot be equidistant from P, as the ground is uneven. AB is 22m, ∠PAB is 34° and ∠PBA is 50°. Calculate the distances:

a) PA   **b)** PB.

If A is level with P and the angle of elevation of F from A is 49°, calculate:

c) FA   **d)** PF.

Q10 An aircraft leaves A and flies 257 km to B on a bearing of 257°. It then flies on to C, 215 km away on a bearing of 163° from B. Calculate:

a) ∠ABC

b) distance CA

c) the bearing needed to fly from A direct to C.

Q11 On my clock the hour hand is 5.5 cm, the minute hand 8 cm and the second hand 7 cm, measured from the centre. Calculate the distance between the tips of the:

a) hour and minute hands at 10 o'clock

b) minute and second hands 15 seconds before 20 past the hour

c) hour and minute hands at 1020.

So the minute hand is at 19.75 minutes past the hour.

Q12 A surveyor wants to measure the height of a building. She measures the angle of elevation of the top of the building from the two different positions shown. Calculate the height of the building to the nearest metre.

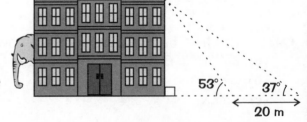

Q13 Mary and Jane were standing one behind the other, 2.3 m apart, each holding one of the two strings of a kite flying directly in front of them. The angles of elevation of the kite from the girls were 65° and 48° respectively. Assuming the ends of both strings are held at the same height above the ground, calculate the length of each string.

More Circle Geometry

Q1 ABCD is a cyclic quadrilateral with angle BCD = 100°.
EF is a tangent to the circle touching it at A.
Angle DAF = 30°.
Write down the size of angle:
a) BAD
b) EAB.

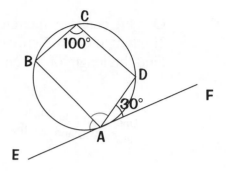

Q2 A, B, and C are points on the circumference of a circle with
centre O. BD and CD are tangents of the circle.
a) State the length BD.
b) Calculate the angle COD.
c) State the angle COB.
d) Find the angle CAB.

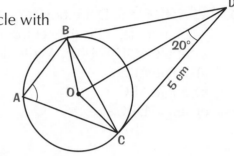

Q3 A, B, C, D and E are points on the circumference of
a circle with centre O. Angle BDE = 53°. The line
AF is a tangent to the circle, touching it at A.
Angle EAF = 32°. Find:
a) angle BOE
b) angle ACE.

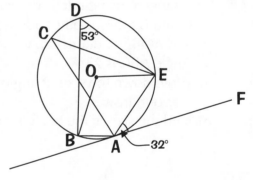

Q4 ABCD is a cyclic quadrilateral and the tangent
to the circle at A makes an angle of 70° with the
side AD. Angle BCA = 30°. Write down, giving
a reason, the size of:
a) angle ACD
b) angle BAD.

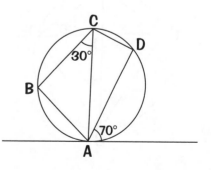

Q5

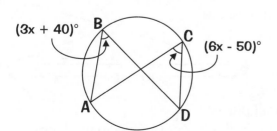

A, B, C and D are points on the
circumference of a circle. Angle ABD
= $(3x + 40)$° and angle ACD = $(6x – 50)$°.
a) Give a reason why angle ABD
and angle ACD are the same.
b) Form an equation in x and by solving it,
find the size of angle ABD.

More Circle Geometry

Q6 O is the centre of a circle and AB is a chord.
The length OA = 5 cm and angle OAB = 20°.
Find the length of the chord AB.

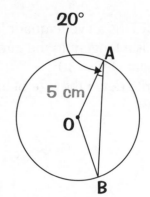

One way to do this is to work out angle AOB and use the sine rule.

Q7 A, B, C and D are points on the circumference
of a circle. O is the centre of the circle and
angle AOD = 140°. Write down:

a) angle ABD
b) angle ABC
c) angle DBC.

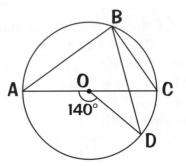

Q8 A tangent of a circle is drawn, touching it at A.
C and B are two other points on the circumference
and AOB is a diameter. O is the centre of the circle.
Angle ABC is 23°.

a) Write down the size of angle ACB, giving a reason
for your answer.
b) Find the size of the angle marked x° in the diagram.

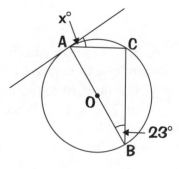

Q9

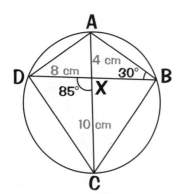

ABCD is a cyclic quadrilateral. The lines AC and BD
intersect at X. Lengths AX = 4 cm, DX = 8 cm and
XC = 10 cm. Angles DXC = 85° and ABD = 30°.

a) Show that triangles DXC and AXB are similar.
b) Find the length of XB.
c) Write down the size of angle BDC.

Q10 B, C and D are three points on the circumference of
a circle with BD as a diameter. O is the centre of the
circle and ADC is a straight line.
AB = 10 cm and BC = 3 cm.

a) Write down the size of angle ACB, giving a
reason for your answer.
b) Show that AC is 9.54 cm correct to 2 decimal places.
c) If AD = 5 cm, find the length of the diameter DOB correct to 2 decimal places.

UNIT 3 — NUMBER, ALGEBRA & GEOMETRY 2

Vectors

Q1 ABCDE is a pentagon.

$$\overrightarrow{AB} = \begin{pmatrix} 3 \\ 3 \end{pmatrix} \quad \overrightarrow{AC} = \begin{pmatrix} 2 \\ 6 \end{pmatrix} \quad \overrightarrow{AD} = \begin{pmatrix} {}^-2 \\ 6 \end{pmatrix} \quad \overrightarrow{AE} = \begin{pmatrix} {}^-3 \\ 2 \end{pmatrix}$$

a) Draw this pentagon accurately.

b) Write down the vectors:

    i) $\overrightarrow{DE}$ **ii)** $\overrightarrow{DC}$ **iii)** $\overrightarrow{EC}$

c) What sort of triangle is Δ ACD?

Q2 $\underline{p} = \begin{pmatrix} 2 \\ 3 \end{pmatrix}, \ \underline{q} = \begin{pmatrix} 0 \\ -2 \end{pmatrix}, \ \underline{r} = \begin{pmatrix} 3 \\ -1 \end{pmatrix}, \ \underline{s} = \begin{pmatrix} -1 \\ -2 \end{pmatrix}$

    Calculate then draw the resultant vectors of:

a) $\underline{p} + \underline{q}$ **c)** $2\underline{r}$ **e)** $2\underline{p} - 2\underline{s}$ **g)** $2\underline{r} - \underline{q}$ **i)** $\underline{p} + 2\underline{s}$

b) $\underline{p} - \underline{q}$ **d)** $\underline{s} + \underline{p}$ **f)** $3\underline{q} + \underline{s}$ **h)** $\frac{1}{2}\underline{q} + 2\underline{r}$ **j)** $\underline{q} - 2\underline{r}$

Q3

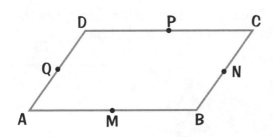

ABCD is a parallelogram. M, N, P and Q are the mid-points of the sides, as shown.

$\overrightarrow{MQ} = \underline{x}$ and $\overrightarrow{AM} = \underline{y}$.

Express in terms of $\underline{x}$ and $\underline{y}$:

a) $\overrightarrow{AB}$ **c)** $\overrightarrow{NB}$ **e)** $\overrightarrow{AC}$

b) $\overrightarrow{AQ}$ **d)** $\overrightarrow{BC}$ **f)** $\overrightarrow{BD}$

Q4 In the diagram on the right, EB and AC are perpendicular. ABCE is a parallelogram. $\angle$EDC is a right angle.

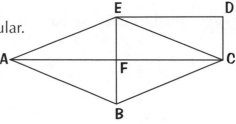

a) Name a vector equal to:

    i) $\overrightarrow{FC}$ **iii)** $\overrightarrow{BC}$ **v)** $2\overrightarrow{CD}$ **vii)** $\overrightarrow{EF} - \overrightarrow{CF}$

    ii) $\overrightarrow{FB}$ **iv)** $\overrightarrow{CE}$ **vi)** $\overrightarrow{AE} + \overrightarrow{EC}$ **viii)** $\overrightarrow{ED} + \overrightarrow{DC} + \overrightarrow{CB}$

b) If AC = 16 cm and EB = 6 cm:
    i) what is the area of ABCE?
    ii) what is the area of ABCDE?

"Real Life" Vector Questions

Look at the pretty pictures... make sure you can see how this little lot fit with the questions.

Q1 In still water my motor boat can achieve 9 km/h. I aim the boat directly across the river which is running at 3 km/h. What is my resultant speed?

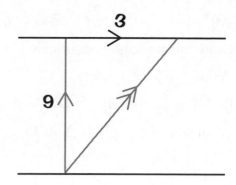

Q2

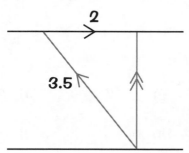

Casey is taking part in a swimming race across a river. The river flows at 2 km/h. Casey can swim at 3.5 km/h.

a) What angle to the bank should she swim to go directly across the river and have the best chance of winning?

b) Calculate her resultant speed.

Q3 An aircraft is attempting to fly due north. The plane travels at 600 km/h, but the pilot has to compensate for a strong 75 km/h wind from the west, as shown.

a) What bearing should the pilot fly the plane on to avoid being blown off course?

b) Calculate the aircraft's resultant speed.

Remember — bearings are measured clockwise from the north line.

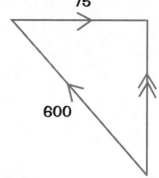

Q4 In the following diagrams, forces are acting on an object as shown.

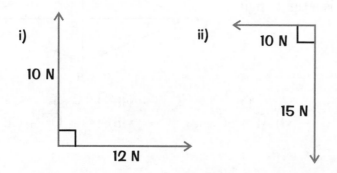

i) 10 N, 12 N

ii) 10 N, 15 N

iii) 23N, 20N

Find the resultant force on each object.

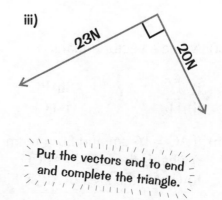

Put the vectors end to end and complete the triangle.

UNIT 3 — NUMBER, ALGEBRA & GEOMETRY 2

The Four Transformations

Only 4 of these to learn... and good old TERRY's always around to help if you need him.

Q1 Copy the axes and mark on triangle A with corners (-1, 2), (0, 4) and (-2, 4). Use a scale of 1 cm to 1 unit.

a) Reflect A in the line $y = -x$.
Label this image B.

b) Reflect A in the line $x = 1$.
Label the image C.

c) Reflect A in the line $y = -1$.
Label the image D.

d) Translate triangle D with the vector $\binom{4}{2}$.
Label this image E.

e) Translate triangle C with the vector $\binom{3}{-3}$.
Label this image F.

f) Describe fully the rotation that sends C to E.

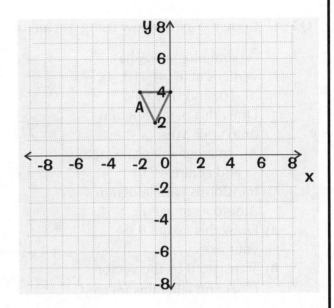

It helps to label the corners of the triangle so you can see exactly what goes where when you do the transformations.

Q2 Copy the axes using a scale of 1 cm to 1 unit. Mark on the axes a quadrilateral Q with corners (-2, 1), (-3, 1), (-3, 3) and (-2, 3).

a) Rotate Q clockwise through 90° about the point (-1, 2). Label the image R.

b) Rotate R clockwise through 90° about the point (0, 1). Label the image S.

c) Describe fully the rotation that maps Q to S.

d) Rotate Q through 180° about the point (-½, -1). Label the image T.

e) Rotate Q anticlockwise through 90° about the point (-1, -1). Label the image U.

f) Describe fully the rotation that sends U to T.

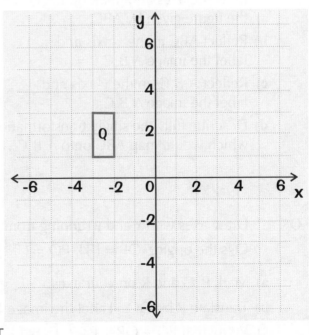

The Four Transformations

Move each point separately — then check your shape hasn't done anything unexpected while you weren't looking.

Q3 Copy the axes below using a scale of 1 cm to 1 unit.

A parallelogram A has vertices at (6, 4), (10, 4), (8, 10) and (12, 10). Draw this parallelogram onto your axes. An enlargement scale factor ½ and centre (0, 0) transforms parallelogram A onto its image B.

a) Draw this image B on your axes.

b) Translate B by the vector $\left(\begin{smallmatrix} -3 \\ -2 \end{smallmatrix}\right)$ and label this image C.

c) Calculate the ratio of the area of parallelogram C to the area of parallelogram A.

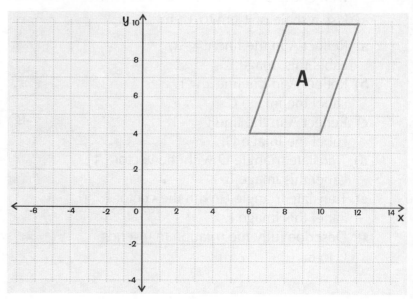

Q4 A is the point (4, 3), B is (4, 1) and C is (5, 1).

a) Using a scale of 1 cm to 1 unit draw the axes and mark on it the figure given by ABC.

b) Reflect ABC in the *x*-axis and label the image $A_1B_1C_1$.

c) Reflect $A_1B_1C_1$ in the *y*-axis and label the image $A_2B_2C_2$.

d) Describe fully the single transformation which would map ABC onto $A_2B_2C_2$.

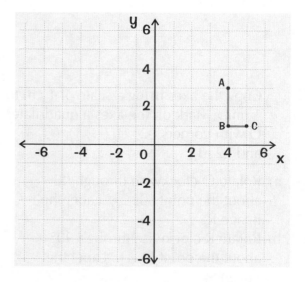

Q5 Draw axes with *x* and *y* running from 0 to 12 with a scale of 1 cm to 1 unit.

O is the origin. $\overrightarrow{OP} = \left(\begin{smallmatrix} 4 \\ 2 \end{smallmatrix}\right)$, $\overrightarrow{PQ} = \left(\begin{smallmatrix} -1 \\ 2 \end{smallmatrix}\right)$, and $\overrightarrow{QR} = 2\overrightarrow{OP}$.

a) Mark P, Q and R on your axes.

b) Translate R by $\overrightarrow{QO}$. Label the image T.

c) Verify that $\overrightarrow{PQ} + \overrightarrow{QR} + \overrightarrow{RT} + \overrightarrow{TP} = O$.

Urghh — vectors...
Make sure you get the
coordinates the right way
round — top for x dirⁿ,
bottom for y dirⁿ.

Congruence and Similarity

Q1   Which pair of triangles are congruent? Explain why.

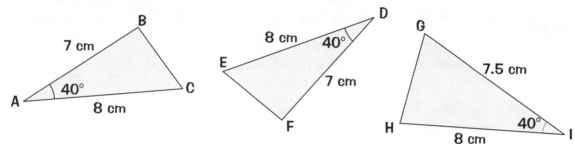

Q2   In the diagram below, BC is parallel to DE.
AB = 12 cm, BD = 8 cm, DE = 25 cm and CE = 10 cm.

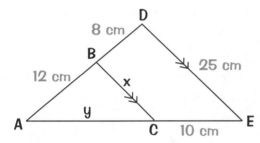

a) Explain why triangles ABC and ADE are similar.
b) Find the lengths of x and y in the diagram.

Q3   Another triangle, congruent to the triangle shown on the
right, must be drawn with vertices at three of the dots.
Show in how many different ways this can be done.

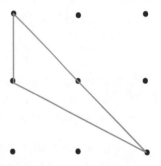

Q4   A cylindrical bottle can hold 1 litre of oil. A second cylindrical bottle
has twice the radius but the same height. It also contains oil.
a) Explain why these bottles are not similar.
b) How much oil can the larger bottle hold?

Q5   A boy made a symmetrical framework with metal rods as shown. Lengths AB = BC,
ST = TC and AP = PQ. Angle BVC = 90° and length BV = 9 cm.

a) Find two triangles which are similar to
triangle ABC.
b) Calculate the length of AP. Hence write
down the length of PT.
c) Calculate the area of triangle ABC.
d) Find the area of triangle APQ. Give your
answer correct to 3 significant figures.
e) Hence write down the area of PQBST
correct to 2 significant figures.

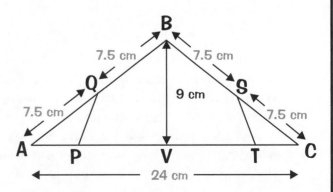

Loci and Construction

Don't let a silly word like <u>locus</u> put you off — there are <u>easy marks</u> to be had here, but you've got to do everything neatly, using a pencil, ruler and compasses.

Q1   Accurately construct an equilateral triangle with sides 4 cm.

Q2 a) Construct a rectangle, 6 cm by 4 cm, and label it as shown.

b) Inside the rectangle:

   i) draw the locus of points 5 cm from D

   ii) draw the locus of points equidistant from A and D

   iii) indicate by an X, the point inside the rectangle
      which is 5 cm from D and equidistant from A and D.

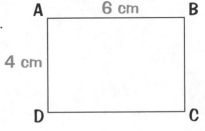

Q3   Construct triangle PQR accurately with length PQ = 10.5 cm,
angle PQR = 95° and angle RPQ = 32°.

a) Construct the perpendicular bisector of the line PR.
Draw in point A where the bisector crosses the line PQ.

b) Bisect angle PRQ. Draw in point B where the bisector
crosses the line PQ. Measure the length BA.

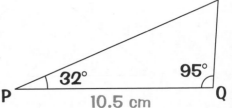

Q4   Omar is doing some garden landscaping.
Because of gas and water pipes, he is not allowed
to dig anywhere within 3 m of his house.

Using a scale of 1 cm to 1 m, draw a diagram for
Omar showing the walls of his house and the area
in which he cannot dig.

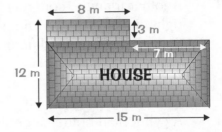

Q5   Construct triangle PQR with length PQ = QR = 11.5 cm
and angle PQR = 38°.

a) Construct the bisectors of angles QPR and QRP.
Mark the point O where the 2 bisectors cross.

b) With centre O draw the circle which just touches the
sides PQ, PR and QR of the triangle. What is the radius
of this circle?

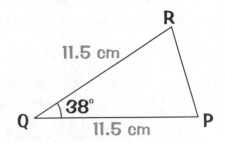

Q6   A and B are 2 points on a straight shore, 4 km apart with A due west of B.

a) Describe the locus of points P such that angle APB equals 90°.

b) Using a scale of 2 cm to 1 km draw an accurate scale diagram
showing A, B, the shore line and the locus of P.
An outcrop of rock is located on a bearing of 060° from A and 300° from B.

c) Indicate the rock on your diagram. Mark the spot with an X.

d) A ship steaming due east parallel to the shore avoids the rock by following the locus of P.
How near does the ship come to the rock?

> Think about your
> geometry rules.

Loci and Construction

Just to be really awkward, the loci of points don't always make a nice line — they can cover a whole area... and you're gonna be asked to shade areas containing all the points.

Q7 This is a plan of Simon's room.

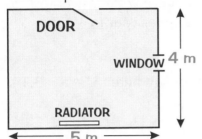

To keep warm Simon must be within 2 m of the wall with the radiator on. To see out of the window he must be within 1.5 m of the wall containing the window.

a) Using a scale of 2 cm to 1 m draw a plan of Simon's room.

b) Shade the region in which Simon must be if he is to be warm and see out of the window.

Q8 A running track is designed so that each point on the track is 32.5 m from a fixed line AB which is 100 m long.

A   100 m   B

a) Draw the locus of the line.

b) Calculate the distance once round the running track.

Q9 Jim is landscaping his back garden, and has drawn the plan below. Two sides of the garden are bounded by fences and the other sides are bounded by the walls of the house and garage. The garden is in the shape of a rectangle.

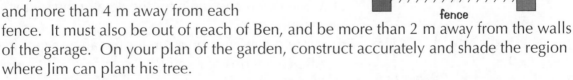

a) Using a scale of 1 cm to 1 m draw a plan of Jim's garden.

b) Ben, the family dog, will be tethered to the garage at B by a lead of length 6 m. Construct accurately and shade the part of the garden where Ben can go.

c) Jim wants to plant a tree in the garden. The tree must be planted more than 5 m away from the walls of the house and more than 4 m away from each fence. It must also be out of reach of Ben, and be more than 2 m away from the walls of the garage. On your plan of the garden, construct accurately and shade the region where Jim can plant his tree.

Q10 The positions of two islands A and B are found from the following information:
A is 35 km from a jetty J on a bearing 065°, B is due south of A and on a bearing of 132° from J as shown below.

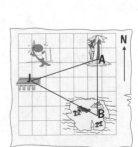

a) Using a scale of 1 cm to 5 km, draw an accurate plan to show the positions of J, A and B.

b) Find from your drawing the distance in km between the islands A and B.

c) A boat leaves the jetty at 09.00 and reaches A at 11.30. What is its average speed in km/h?

d) A lightship L is 20 km from J, equidistant from A and B and on the same side of J as A and B. Mark L on the drawing.

e) Find the bearing of L from J.

Circles, Cylinders and Spheres

Q1 Using π = 3.14, find:
  a) The area of a circle with radius = 6.12 m. Give your answer <u>to 3 dp</u>.
  b) The circumference of a circle with radius = 7.2 m. Give your answer <u>to 2 sf</u>.
  c) The circumference of a circle with diameter = 14.8 m. Give your answer <u>to 1 dp</u>.
  d) The area of a circle with diameter = 4.246 cm. Give answer your <u>to 3 dp</u>.

Q2 Find the <u>area and the perimeter</u> of each of the shapes drawn here. Use π = 3.14.

  a)

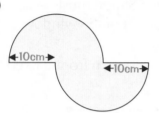

  b)

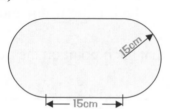

  c)

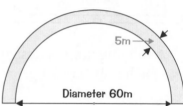

Q3 A plastic strip is made in the shape shown.
  The curves AC and BD are both arcs of
  circles with centre O. The larger circle has
  radius 30 mm and the smaller circle has
  radius 20 mm. The shaded ends of the shape
  are both semicircles.

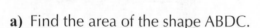

  a) Find the area of the shape ABDC.
  b) Find the area of the two semicircular ends.
      Hence write down the area of the complete shape.

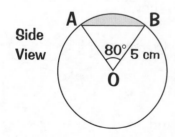

Suppose the radius of the arc AC is now r and that
of BD is R.
  c) Write down a formula for the area of the sector OBD
     in terms of R.
  d) Write down an expression for the area of the shape
     ABDC in terms of r and R.
  e) Hence write down an expression for the area of the
     complete shape.

Q4

A washing powder ball looks from the side like a
circle with the shaded area removed. The circle
has radius 5 cm and the angle AOB = 80°.
  a) Find the area of the sector OAB.
  b) Find the area of triangle AOB and hence the area
     of the shaded area.

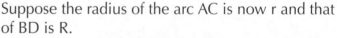

The formula you
need for part b) is
area = ½absinC.

Circles, Cylinders and Spheres

Make sure you know the <u>4 main volume formulas</u> —
for <u>spheres</u>, <u>cylinders</u>, <u>cones and frustums</u>.

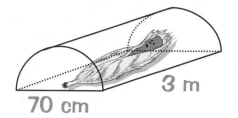

Q5   Joe buys a polythene tunnel to protect his plants
from frost. It has a semicircular diameter of
70 cm and a length of 3 m.
a) Find the cross-sectional area.
b) Hence find the volume of the tunnel.

Q6   I am planning to build a circular pond in my garden
surrounded by a ring shaped paved area.
The pond will be 50 cm deep and filled with water.
a) Calculate the approximate cost of paving the area around
the pond with slabs costing £16 per m².
Give your answer to the nearest £10.
b) I need to add 15 ml of liquid pond treatment for every m³ of
water in the pond. Find the volume of treatment I will need
to add to the pond. Give your answer to the nearest ml.

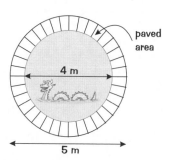

Q7   A solid metal cube, each of whose sides
is 10 cm long, is melted down and made
into a solid cylinder 10 cm high.
a) What is the radius of this cylinder?
b) Find the surface area of the cylinder.

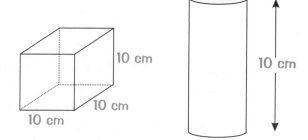

Q8   A tin mug has the dimensions shown.
a) What is the greatest volume of milk the
mug can hold?
b) In fact, 600 cm³ of milk is poured in.
How high will it go up the mug?

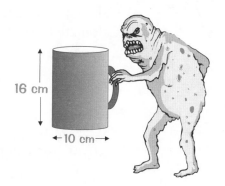

Q9

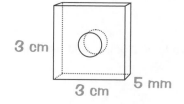

A nut has the cross-section illustrated.
The circular hole has a diameter of
1.4 cm and the nut is 5 mm thick.
Find the volume of the nut in cm³.

(Units...)

Circles, Cylinders and Spheres

Q10 Davey is pumping up a basketball. He knows the diameter of a fully-inflated basketball should be no more than 30 cm. Calculate the maximum volume of air that Davey should use to inflate his basketball.

Q11

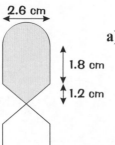

2.6 cm

1.8 cm

1.2 cm

An egg timer is symmetrical and consists of hemispheres, cylinders and cones joined together as shown to the left.

a) Calculate the volume of sand in the upper container.

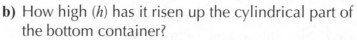
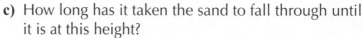

You need to find three volumes and add them together.

Sand runs into the bottom container at a constant rate of 0.05 cm³ per second. At the end of a certain time period the sand has fallen through into the bottom container as shown to the right.

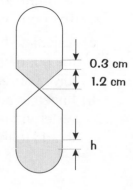

0.3 cm

1.2 cm

h

b) How high (*h*) has it risen up the cylindrical part of the bottom container?

c) How long has it taken the sand to fall through until it is at this height?

Q12

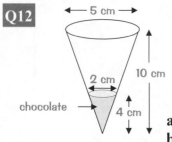

5 cm

2 cm

10 cm

chocolate

4 cm

An ice-cream cone is 10 cm deep and has a base diameter of 5 cm. The bottom 4 cm of the cone is filled with solid chocolate as shown. The rest of the cone is filled with ice cream and a hemisphere of ice cream is mounted on top so that the base of the hemisphere coincides with the base of the cone.

a) Calculate the volume of ice cream required to make one ice cream.

b) Calculate the outer surface area of the cone.

Q13

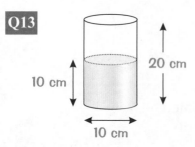

20 cm

10 cm

10 cm

Mike and Shelly are doing an experiment to find the radius of a marble. They fill a cylindrical container of diameter 10 cm and height 20 cm with water to a depth of 10 cm. 200 identical marbles are now submerged in the water. The depth increases to 14.5 cm. Calculate the radius of one marble.

The volume increase is a cylinder and you're told the height.

Area, Volume and Density

Don't forget that when you're enlarging areas and volumes,
there's a bigger scale factor — that one catches everyone out.

Q1 The area of a square is 9000 m².
   a) What is the length of a <u>side</u>? (to 2 dp)
   b) What is the <u>perimeter</u> of the square? (to 2 dp)

Q2 The large rectangles in diagrams A and B (below) are similar. The small
rectangles in the diagrams below are also similar. Find the shaded area of B.

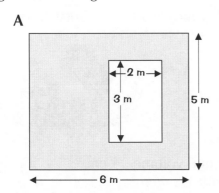
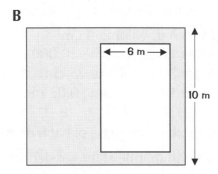

Q3 Two cups A and B are similar. Cup A has a height of 15 cm and cup B has a
height of 5 cm. Cup A has a volume of 54 cm³. Calculate the volume of cup B.

Q4 The two cereal boxes shown below are similar.

Calculate the difference in
volume between the boxes.

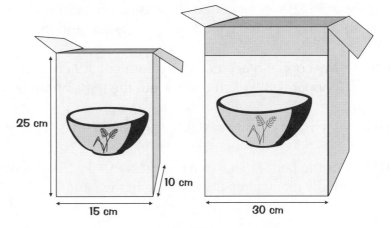

Q5 Sharon has a fish tank which is 42 cm wide
and has a volume of 30 litres. She sees a
similar fish tank in the pet shop which is
63 cm wide. What is the volume of the
larger fish tank to the nearest litre?

Area, Volume and Density

Here we go again — the multi-purpose formula triangle. Learn the positions of M, D and V, plug in the numbers and pull out the answer... magic.

$$\text{DENSITY} = \frac{\text{mass}}{\text{volume}}$$

Q6 Find the <u>density</u> of each of these pieces of wood, giving your answer in g/cm³:

a) Mass 3 g, volume 4 cm³
b) Mass 12 kg, volume 20,000 cm³
c) Mass 20 g, volume 25 cm³
d) Mass 14 kg, volume 0.02 m³.

Q7 Calculate the <u>mass</u> of each of these objects:

a) a small marble statue of density 2.6 g/cm³ and volume 24 cm³
b) a plastic cube of volume 64 cm³ and density 1.5 g/cm³
c) a gold ingot measuring 12 cm by 4 cm by 4 cm with density 19.5 g/cm³
d) a pebble with volume 30 cm³ and density 2.5 g/cm³.

Q8 Work out the <u>volume</u> of each of these items:
a) a bag of sugar of mass 1 kg and density 1.6 g/cm³
b) a packet of margarine with density 2.8 g/cm³ and mass 250 g
c) a 50 kg sack of coal with density 1.8 g/cm³
d) a box of cereal with density 0.2 g/cm³ and mass 500 g.

Q9 My copper bracelet has a volume of 3.9 cm³. The density of copper is 8.9 g/cm³. Work out the <u>mass</u> of my bracelet.

Q10 Ice has a density of 0.93 g/cm³. If the mass of a block of ice is 19.5 kg, what is its <u>volume</u>?

Q11 Some petrol in a can has a mass of 4 kg. The density of the petrol is 0.8 g/cm³. How many <u>litres</u> of petrol are in the can?

1 litre = 1000 cm³.

Q12 A jug holds 1.9 litres of lemonade. The mass of the lemonade is 2 kg. Find the <u>density</u> of the lemonade. Give your answer in g/cm³.

Q13 A 1.5 kg bag full of self-raising flour measures 12 cm by 18 cm by 6 cm. A 1 kg bag of granary flour measures 10 cm by 14 cm by 6 cm.
a) Find the <u>density</u> of each sort of flour.
b) Jake needs to measure out 450 g of granary flour but his scales are broken. Use your answer to part a) to work out how much flour he should measure out in his measuring jug. Give your answer in ml.

1 ml = 1 cm³